DBT Workbool

Proven Psychological Techniques for Managing Trauma & Emotional Healing with Dialectical Behavior Therapy

DBT Skills to Treat Post-Traumatic Stress Disorder for Men & Women

By Barrett Huang

https://barretthuang.com/

Table of Contents

Introduction

"There is no timestamp on trauma. There isn't a formula that you can insert yourself into to get from horror to healed. Be patient. Take up space. Let your journey be the balm."
– Dawn Serra

I was a very troubled and lonely teen. My parents moved from China to Canada to provide a better life for our family. But I looked different, talked differently, and even the food I ate was different. So, growing up, I never felt like I belonged—anywhere. Even today, as an adult, it's very hard for me to describe the pain that comes from loneliness. But that's not all.

My father was a hoarder who had Obsessive Compulsive Disorder (OCD). My mother suffered from severe anxiety and showed PTSD symptoms due to a childhood accident (more on that later). Because of all the chaos and instability at home and the loneliness and isolation I felt as a teenager, and it's no surprise that I was diagnosed with OCD and General Anxiety Disorder (GAD) as an adult. And although I was not clinically diagnosed with it, I knew I also suffered from depression.

I knew I had to do something when I left home for college. Although I didn't fully understand what was going on with me, I knew this to be true: something had to change because I couldn't go on with life that way.

I started seeing a mental health professional and was prescribed anti-anxiety medication. It somewhat improved my ability to handle daily life. However, this was only the start of my journey.

I tried different types of therapy. But the one that worked for me, allowing me to cope and overcome my various mental health issues, is the one I am sharing in this book—Dialectical Behavior Therapy (DBT).

During one of the DBT group therapy sessions, I met Paul* and learned about his post-traumatic stress disorder (PTSD).

Content Warning: the following story contains potentially distressing material.

> *"I was about 16 years old, I think. I was working part-time at a popular coffee shop in the city center. One payday, I and a bunch of other teens working there decided we'd treat ourselves to a burger and movie that night. We were going to watch The Matrix!*
>
> *It was a great and fun night... until it wasn't.*
>
> *After the movie, I gallantly escorted one of the girls home. She was just a few blocks from the cinema anyway. From there, I had to walk back and take the subway back home.*
>
> *I didn't notice anything at all after I dropped her off. I turned a corner, and suddenly a group of guys was on me. To this day, I don't remember how many.*
>
> *Even though I wasn't beaten to a pulp, I was shoved around roughly enough to know that this was serious. All of a sudden, someone took out a gun.*

---

* *Name changed for privacy.*

I don't remember what was said or what happened in what order. What I remember, always so clearly, was how the cold, hard barrel of the gun felt against my temple.

They wanted my wallet, but I remember hands patting me up and down, over and over, everywhere. Many years later, I would process this part as sexual assault.

After taking my wallet, they laughed as they left.

I don't remember how I got home. I remember locking my bedroom door shut. I would do this every night from that moment on.

The following morning, I went down for breakfast, and I remember my mom asking how last night had gone. I remember taking a moment before I looked up and said, "It was great!"

I didn't decide beforehand to keep what happened a secret. I guess, when confronted, I just wanted to forget about it. I was young enough to foolishly think, "If no one knows, it didn't happen."

But it did happen, and I've been living with it since. I don't want to, but I do."

Paul had a tough time after that traumatic incident. One of the things he mentioned during therapy that struck me so much was when he said, *"After what happened, it's like "Paul" disappeared, and I don't know why."*

Just like me, Paul went through years of loneliness, anger, shame, frustration, fear, depression, severe anxiety, and others. His life was an endless story of failed relationships and attempts to keep a job. Paul was eventually diagnosed with PTSD and tried various therapies before trying DBT.

Since that first DBT group therapy session, Paul and I have become friends. We've seen each other through some tough times in our lives, and I'm happy to say that today, Paul and I no longer see ourselves as "just surviving" but as "survivors."

So, why did I write this book? Well, as cliché as it sounds, I want to help.

One component of mental health disorders that Paul, myself, and a significant number of people discuss is that, for years, we don't understand what's going on with ourselves.

If you're hungry, you ask for food. If you're thirsty, you ask for something to drink. If you have a mental health problem, you might not even know you should be asking for something, let alone know what to ask for.

We don't have the vocabulary to describe what we're going through. We're not equipped to look at ourselves and how we should start healing. And even if there's some awareness, we don't know what to do about it.

We don't start to understand things until much later. And this only happens if we are lucky enough to: 1) realize that life can be better, 2) know we need help, 3) ask for, seek, or be open to help, and 4) use the help we get.

Today, as an adult, I often look back at my teenage self and feel a lot of empathy. If only that kid understood that his parents were suffering from mental health problems and that his chaotic, traumatic, and unbalanced home life was not normal. If only that teen understood how "not belonging" left him empty. If only he knew what to do to start making friends in a strange country, then perhaps he wouldn't have spent years being lonely and depressed.

As an adult, Paul knows that he couldn't have known what would happen that night and that he's lucky to be still alive. However, as a teenager, *"How do you even begin to describe the feeling of having a gun to your head? Even now, I have trouble putting it in words."* He also knows that he is a victim and shouldn't feel shame. But as a teen, *"Just the thought of telling someone that grown men touched me all over made me want to throw up."*

So I wrote this book to help you.

- I want to help you know **you're not the only one going through this**.
- I want to help you **see your incredible strength** for coming this far. That you have this book in your hands speaks volumes of your courage because confronting trauma is nothing but an act of bravery.
- I want to help you realize that **you're not broken but are hurt** and need support, compassion, and kindness.
- I want to help you **live the life you want to live**.

I will not sugar-coat it. You deserve honesty. The journey to healing from PTSD, or any mental health disorder, is never a linear process. There will be ups, and there will be downs. But this I promise you: keep at it, and you'll always be going forward.

But where do you start? What do you do? How do you proceed? Hopefully, this DBT for PTSD book provides the answers you seek.

Who Should Read This Book

This book is for anyone who has suffered trauma. You might be showing PTSD symptoms or have already been diagnosed with PTSD. You may be undergoing therapy and want to use this book and its exercises as part of your healing, or you may want to go through this material yourself. Either way, you want to address at least one aspect of the trauma you experienced or witnessed to lessen its impact on your life.

This book is also for anyone with a partner, friend, or family member exhibiting PTSD symptoms or diagnosed with it. Understanding is one of the first steps we can take to help and support anyone living with PTSD.

Goals of This Book

This book aims to teach you Dialectical Behavior Therapy (DBT) skills and how to use them to deal with the stress symptoms associated with trauma. Within these pages are mindfulness, stress coping, emotion regulation, and interpersonal exercises and techniques to help you feel better.

How to Use This Book

The first part of this book introduces PTSD, what it is, its causes, what happens inside and outside of your body, etc. Trauma is a very sensitive topic that is often misunderstood. So to move forward, I believe it's essential to know what you want to move forward from.

The second part of this book discusses DBT (e.g., its history, what it's all about, what to expect, why it can help with PTSD, and so on). Here, you'll understand what makes DBT different from other forms of therapy and why it's an excellent means to address PTSD.

The third part of this book discusses using DBT skills to help you deal with PTSD. You see, learning is not just reading and gaining information. Real learning happens when you put what you've just learned to use and do something with it.

So this part of the book is full of step-by-step DBT exercises designed to help with PTSD.

Content Warning

Please note that this book contains content that might be troubling to some readers. Some stories, topics, and examples might be considered distressing material that can trigger adverse reactions. Content may include but is not limited to childhood trauma, adult trauma, abandonment, self-harm, anxiety, emotional abuse, mental illness, eating disorders, night terrors, and others. Please be mindful of these and other possible triggers. Above all, never hesitate to seek assistance or professional help when you need it.

Safety

What does it mean to be safe? What does "safety" look or feel like to you? This book talks about trauma and how to deal with its repercussions. In going over its content, it's essential to *be safe* and *feel safe*. Here are some tips:

- Think about moments in your life when you felt safe, and write about them in as much detail as possible. Whenever you feel any unpleasant emotions or reactions, turn to your journal and let the memory and feeling of safety come over you.
- Know your safety vulnerabilities. For example, if the traumatic event occurred at night, go over this book and its exercises during the day. If the traumatic event resulted in you fearing for your physical safety, then perhaps you should not be alone when you go over this book and its exercises. Visit the library or sit down at a local café.
- Plan B. Write down what you should do when you start feeling unsafe. Here are a few ideas:

- Stop and take a walk in nature.
- Call ___________________.
- Stop and hug your pet.
- Look at a picture of _________________.
- Stop and listen to __________________.
- Others:

  ____

  ____

  ____

  ____

  ____

  ____

About Me

"I'm not saying I will heal you.
But I am sharing what healed me." – Barrett Huang

My journey into mental healing has inspired me to learn more about the mind and behavior. So I majored in psychology and have completed the DBT Skills certificate program of Dr. Marsha Linehan, the founder of DBT. I have also taken to heart Dr. Linehan's philosophy of "living a life worth living." So I've spent years broadening my philosophy, happiness, and self-improvement knowledge. Still, I'd like to emphasize that the contents of this book draw primarily from my personal struggles with mental health disorders and the struggles of people I know that are gracious enough to allow me to share their stories. DBT has helped us cope, survive, and thrive. I sincerely hope that it helps you as you take your own journey to mental healing.

You Can Feel Better

You and I know that life is not easy. Add traumatic experiences into the mix, and life becomes even more difficult. But there is hope. You can feel better.

When I was suffering from my mental health problems, I was lost and constantly struggling. I felt like I was living in a tiny, very tight maze that I didn't want to be in but couldn't get out of. The following pages taught me how to get out of that maze.

I can honestly say I have never felt better about myself and my life as I do today. And I wholeheartedly believe the same can happen to you. All you need to do now is turn the page, start your journey, and keep going until you're free from your maze.

Chapter 1: What is PTSD?

"PTSD: It's not the person refusing to let go of the past, but the past refusing to let go of the person." – Anonymous

Post	Traumatic	Stress	Disorder
After	Trauma	Stress	Irregular Function of Mind or Body

Post-traumatic stress disorder (PTSD) is a specific set of reactions that can develop in anyone who has ever experienced or witnessed a terrible, distressing event that threatened their life, safety, or the lives of people around them.

PTSD was once thought only to affect war veterans. This was because soldiers who returned home from war showed high levels of stress, depression, anxiety, fear, and other physical and psychological problems. Terms such as "shell shock," "combat fatigue," and "war neurosis" were coined.

In the 1980s, however, the American Psychiatric Association officially recognized "post-traumatic stress disorder" in the third edition of its Diagnostic and Statistical Manual of Mental Disorders (DSM-III). This is a turning point in the history of PTSD because it highlights that a traumatic event triggers the mental condition. In short, a person does not cause PTSD; a traumatic event does. Trauma is at the core of PTSD.

Trauma can happen anytime. How many times have you started your day feeling happy and awesome, and then something happens that changes the course of your life forever?

Content Warning: the following story contains potentially distressing material.

My friend Myrah[†] *has this to say: "Greg and I have been married for 11 wonderful years. We have a 7-year-old daughter. We've been trying for a second child for years, but it seemed like it wouldn't happen anymore, so Greg and I eventually said to each other, "We have a great daughter. Our little family of three is more than enough."*

Nearly a year later, my belly started to hurt unexpectedly, and I began to bleed a bit. I thought I had a bad PMS case (premenstrual syndrome). The following day, I went to work and had the most horrendous pain in my belly in the middle of a meeting. I also started bleeding a lot. I was rushed to the hospital, and after a thorough examination, I discovered I had just had a miscarriage.

I was stunned. I couldn't speak. Tears just kept falling and falling. I was pregnant, and I didn't know it! I lost a baby I didn't think I had. What did I do wrong?!

I can't describe what happened after because everything was just a blur. I was just in a haze of sadness and agony. Since I couldn't explain how I felt, no one understood the depth of my grieving, not even my husband. Eventually, Greg and I divorced."

Trauma can happen to anyone. It can happen to a child with no defenses or an adult who feels at the peak of their life.

[†] *Name changed for privacy.*

Trauma doesn't have to happen in the "first person." You don't need to experience trauma to develop PTSD personally. Witnessing a traumatic event can also bring about this condition.

For example, the September 11 terrorist attacks[1] on the World Trade Center and the Pentagon in the US were highly traumatic to people on ground zero and those exposed to the event through the enormous and almost non-stop media coverage. People worldwide, not just in the US, suddenly felt scared, unsafe, and uncertain about the future because this was not an accident but *intentional violence*.

Reaction to trauma comes in various shapes and sizes. Why does trauma affect us differently? How can the same event be traumatic for one person but not for another? This is because of our individual personalities, histories, life experiences, and situations.

My friend Myrah (page 15) suffered from clinical depression in her teens. This vulnerability, coupled with the trauma of losing a child who was so desperately wanted, triggered her PTSD.

When the 9/11 attacks occurred, a friend who had *aerophobia* (fear of flying) developed PTSD even though he was nowhere near ground zero. This is called *secondary trauma*.[2]

"Secondary" means that the original (primary) trauma happened to someone else, but the situation is having a traumatic effect on your life nonetheless. Secondary trauma is NOT any less severe or more straightforward to deal with than any other kind of PTSD.

So, even though a traumatic event is an *external phenomenon*, our experience is filtered through our cognitive and emotional processes.

However, despite all of the above variations, one thing is sure: **trauma is anything that endangers your feeling of safety**.

What Causes PTSD?

PTSD can develop after experiencing or witnessing a single distressing, traumatic event (e.g., the unexpected loss of a loved one) or after being consistently exposed to it (e.g., abuse, bullying, etc.).

The following are the types of traumatic events that can lead to PTSD:

- Serious accidents (e.g., being involved in a car crash)
- Criminal activities (e.g., robbery, kidnapping, cybercrime, etc.)
- Sexual assault or abuse (e.g., rape, human trafficking, etc.)
- Physical assault or abuse (e.g., child abuse, spousal abuse, bullying, racism, being kidnapped, being held hostage, etc.)
- The sudden death of someone you love or someone very close to you
- Serious health problems (e.g., being diagnosed with a life-threatening illness)
- Childbirth experiences (e.g., miscarriage, problems during childbirth)
- Witnessing traumatic events over and over due to your job (e.g., cops constantly exposed to gun violence, first responders exposed to life and death situations daily, etc.)
- Natural disasters (e.g., earthquakes, fires, floods, hurricanes, pandemics such as COVID-19, etc.)
- Acts of terrorism (e.g., school shootings, bombings, hijackings, etc.)
- War and conflict
- Torture

Question: I experienced/witnessed one of the items above. Does it mean I have PTSD?

No. It's important to remember that **not everyone who goes through a traumatic event develops PTSD**.

Even though there are situations when exposure to trauma is so great that the chance of developing PTSD is very high (e.g., surviving a car accident in which your whole family perishes, participating in combat, etc.), there are some things that greatly influence it. Here are a few examples.

Before the Trauma

Your personal situation before a traumatic event influences your resilience to trauma. These factors may include the following:

- **Previous exposure to trauma or experiencing emotional problems at a very young age.** For example, say you were bullied every day at school, and despite this, you grew up to be a healthy, happy, and well-adjusted adult. However, you experienced being the victim of a crime and were held at knifepoint. This recent trauma might be the "straw that breaks the camel's back" and cause PTSD.
- A personal or family **history of mental illness**.
- Having **unhealthy and ineffective coping strategies** like blaming yourself when something unpleasant happens.
- A **history of substance abuse**.
- **Problems with school** such as low academic performance, frequent fights with teachers and students, always skipping school, etc.
- **Experience early losses** such as previously losing your home or losing money in an investment gone wrong.
- **Lack of a healthy support system.**

During the Trauma

Factors present during a traumatic event are also relevant. These factors may include the following:

- **Proximity to the trauma.** For example, after 9/11, a study showed that people who were in the New York City metropolitan area during the attack were more likely to develop PTSD than those who were physically further from that area.[3]
- **Suffering an injury.** For example, let's say you and your friends were at the movies when a fire broke out. As you and your friends try to exit the movie house, you trip, get trampled and suffer a broken leg.
- **Personal meaning of the traumatic event**. For example, a person who has grown up with an abusive parent might develop PTSD if they find themselves in an abusive relationship. Note that the type of abuse doesn't have to be the same.

Content Warning: the following story contains potentially distressing material.

My friend Angie[‡] had this to say: *"My father was an alcoholic and was emotionally abusive to my mother. He was never physically or emotionally abusive to us, just my mom. Later, I had a boyfriend who had anger management issues, and one day, in a fit of jealousy, he just lost it. He grabbed me by the shirt, dragged me to the kitchen, and hit me on the head with a frying pan. It happened once, as I ended the relationship immediately after that.*

However, soon after, I started to have panic attacks whenever I heard loud things in the kitchen. I was also constantly in fear. I was afraid of running into my ex every time I left home. It got so bad that I quit my job

---

[‡] *Name changed for privacy.*

and started working online. I ordered food and groceries so I wouldn't have to go out. I avoided my friends.

One day, my mom came to visit, and when I opened the door, she looked at me from head to toe and cried. She was the one who convinced me to seek help.

After undergoing therapy, I learned that unresolved issues from my childhood triggered my PTSD. My father's abuse of my mother always had my siblings and me on pins and needles. For years, we feared he would finally turn on us, and my ex-boyfriend brought that fear into reality."

- **Duration of the trauma.** For example, being held hostage in a bank robbery that lasted for hours.
- **Risk of trauma occurrence.** For example, living in a neighborhood where crime rates are high.
- **Accidental vs. intentional violence**. Domestic abuse, racism, bullying, terrorist attacks, and others leave us more prone to develop PTSD because this type of violence provokes higher emotional responses.[4]
- The **atrocity of the traumatic event**. For example, witnessing a heinous crime.

After the Trauma

Your environment after a traumatic incident also influences the likelihood of developing PTSD. These factors may include the following:

- **Absence of a good support system** (e.g., family, friends, colleagues).

Content Warning: the following story contains potentially distressing material.

One of our readers, Kian[§], said: *"During the pandemic, I lost my mother in the worst circumstances. Like so many others, I wasn't with her and didn't get to say goodbye. I'm an only child, and my father died when I was a baby, so I lost my one and only anchor in this world when she passed away. I was in shock. I was traumatized. I was alone.*

I reached out to a few friends, but they were also dealing with their stuff, so I locked myself in my apartment for a whole year. I didn't talk to anyone, and no one talked to me.

I don't know what I would've done if I had not encountered an online group on DBT. I'm still not where I want to be, but at least now I have some hope I'll get there. "

- **Rumination and feelings of helplessness.** For example, re-living the traumatic event over and over in your head, thinking of the "what ifs," and ending up feeling helpless again.
- **Self-pity or victimizing yourself.** For example, having thoughts of *"Why me?", "What did I do wrong?", "What did I do to deserve this?".*

---

§ *Name changed for privacy.*

- **Self-neglect** or not taking care of yourself. For example, it's understandable that you might lose appetite[5] or have sleep problems[6,7] after a traumatic event. However, if you keep this up, you'll hurt your physical and mental health[8], making you more vulnerable to PTSD.

Many factors affect how you react to a traumatic experience. For instance, if you're an optimistic person, if you've previously handled setbacks and bounced back, and so on.

If you want to quickly check your ability to effectively handle trauma, you can check the Trauma Resiliency exercise on *Appendix A (page 145).*

But, surely, STRESS is a normal reaction to trauma? Yes, absolutely. If you notice that you're agitated or overly cautious after a traumatic event, that's normal. Physical reactions such as sweating or an increased pulse rate are also expected. Emotional responses such as anger or fear are also natural reactions to trauma. It is when everyday stress becomes *distressed*, when your stress lasts way after the traumatic incident is over, or when it becomes severe to the point that it interferes with your health, your relationships, and your daily life—this is when stress evolves into post-traumatic stress disorder (PTSD).

What are the Symptoms of PTSD?

There is no specific timeframe when PTSD symptoms show up after a traumatic event. Some people experience symptoms immediately after the event. For others, it can take months or even years before any symptoms appear (as a result of being triggered).

Since PTSD symptoms can take many different forms, four broad categories or "clusters" have been established by experts: *intrusive symptoms*, *avoidance symptoms*, *negative changes in mood and thoughts*, and *hyper-reactivity (being on edge).*

1) Intrusive Symptoms (Re-Experiencing)

Intrusive symptoms, also known as *re-experiencing*, are when we re-live the trauma we experienced or witnessed whether we want to or not. These may include:

- Unwelcome and frequent recollection of the terrible event.
- Re-living the traumatic experience as though it were happening again (flashbacks).
- Having disturbing nightmares involving the trauma.
- Emotional distress or involuntary physical reactions to something that reminds you of the traumatic event. For example, a woman who has had a miscarriage might suddenly be overcome with extreme sadness and cry uncontrollably when she sees a pregnant woman.

2) Avoidance Symptoms

Avoidance is when we avoid or disengage from anything and everything that might remind us of the trauma we experienced. It is considered a maladaptive (unhealthy) coping mechanism[9]. Still, we do it because it gives our minds an escape from difficult thoughts, feelings, and experiences. These may include:

- Avoiding thinking about or discussing the painful event.
- Avoiding people, places, or things that remind you of the trauma.
- Engaging in distracting activities such as throwing yourself into work or a new hobby.

3) Negative Changes in Mood and Thoughts

This is when we start thinking and feeling unhealthy because of the trauma. These may include:

- Negative thoughts and feelings that lead to incorrect beliefs about oneself (e.g., *"I'm not a good person," "Maybe I deserve what happened,"* etc.)
- Negative thoughts and feelings that lead to incorrect beliefs about others (e.g., *"I can't trust anyone," "Everybody lies,"* etc.)
- Feeling disconnected from other people (alienation).
- Feelings of panic, horror, anger, guilt, or shame that never goes away.
- Unable to feel happiness, contentment, safety, or any other positive emotions.
- Loss of interest in hobbies and activities that you used to find joyful.
- Loss of interest in life in general.

4) Hyper-Reactivity (Being on Edge)

This is when we are over-reactive or display strong reactions to stimuli. These may include:

- Uncontrollable outbursts of anger.
- Being highly aggressive or irritable.
- Engaging in self-destructive or risky behavior (e.g., self-harm, impulsive and reckless sexual behavior, gambling, using alcohol and drugs, etc.)
- Hypervigilance or being overly suspicious of what's happening around you.
- Being easily startled or frightened.
- Unable to focus or sleep because your mind is always in "alert mode."
- Seeing danger everywhere.

Question: I'm experiencing some of the above symptoms. Does it mean I have PTSD?

To be officially diagnosed with PTSD, there must be:

- At least one symptom of re-experiencing or re-living the traumatic event;
- At least one symptom of avoidance;
- At least two symptoms of negative changes in mood and thoughts; and
- At least two symptoms of hyper-reactivity.

The symptoms must last for more than a month and be so severe and distressing that they interfere with your daily life.

Important: Not having an official PTSD diagnosis doesn't mean you don't need help or shouldn't deal with whatever symptom(s) you're experiencing. Self-help or asking for help is always essential and doesn't need to meet any criteria.

What are the Different Types of PTSD?

There are different types of PTSD: *uncomplicated PTSD*, *dissociative PTSD*, *complex PTSD,* and *comorbid PTSD*. Following is a quick breakdown of their differences.

1. Uncomplicated PTSD

Uncomplicated PTSD usually comes from a single traumatic event, as opposed to experiencing multiple or repeating trauma.

For example, someone in a severe car accident might become afraid to drive, get startled when a car honks, get uncontrollably angry while driving, take longer routes to avoid the area where the traumatic car accident happened, and so on.

2. Dissociative PTSD

Dissociation means disconnection. As such, a person with dissociative PTSD is someone diagnosed with PTSD who shows depersonalization (feeling detached from one's own body) or derealisation (viewing things as unreal or dreamlike) symptoms.

For example, a child subjected to abuse and diagnosed with PTSD as an adult might also show symptoms of "blanking out," numbness, inability to connect with others, and so on.

3. Complex PTSD

Complex PTSD, or c-PTSD, is considered the most severe type of this mental health disorder. It's usually caused by experiencing recurring or long-term traumatic events, and symptoms are generally more behavioral.

For example, someone who's suffered domestic abuse for years might develop low self-esteem, anger or rage issues, severe mood instability, and others. They may also develop other mental health problems, such as depression.

4. Comorbid PTSD

Comorbid means "to exist simultaneously." As such, comorbid PTSD is when a person has PTSD in addition to other trauma-related disorders that aren't part of their PTSD diagnosis.

For example, someone with PTSD may also concurrently be diagnosed with generalized anxiety disorder (GAD), major depressive disorder (MDD), borderline personality disorder (BPD), substance abuse problems, and others.

PTSD Treatments

I believe there's no single, one-size-fits-all solution to addressing mental health problems. When I was suffering from OCD, GAD, and depression, I underwent Cognitive Behavioral Therapy (CBT). I was prescribed anti-anxiety medication, which helped jumpstart my healing.

After some time, I adjusted enough that taking prescribed meds was no longer necessary. However, I was still suffering from many mental health challenges. At that point, I knew CBT wasn't what I needed anymore. That's how I discovered and consequently stayed with Dialectical Behavior Therapy (DBT).

So, I guess I'm trying to say that seeking and undergoing treatment is a journey. Helping yourself to get better takes time, so my advice is to, first and foremost, **have an open mind; be curious; be kind to yourself, and give yourself time to heal**.

Following are some of the more known treatments for PTSD today.

Cognitive Behavioral Therapy (CBT)

Cognitive means "mind." As such, Cognitive Behavioral Therapy or CBT focuses on how you process your thoughts and feelings related to the traumatic event and for you to understand your resulting behavior from the trauma.

During therapy, which is usually administered over 12-16 sessions in either individual or group format[10], you might be asked to talk about your traumatic experience and how your thoughts about it affect your daily life.

For example, say you're prone to uncontrollable outbursts of anger due to trauma. CBT can help you understand what goes on inside your mind and body and teach you how to cope with your anger. Another example: suppose you've become afraid and overly pessimistic about people or the world because of the trauma you experienced or witnessed. In that case, CBT will help you re-evaluate these negative thinking patterns.

Prolonged Exposure Therapy (PET)

Prolonged Exposure Therapy (is a specific type of CBT wherein you're taught to slowly face the memories, emotions, and situations related to the trauma. If you remember, Avoidance (page 23) is one of the major symptoms of PTSD. The problem with this symptom is that *avoidance coping* never addresses underlying issues. It's a short-term, Band-Aid solution.

PET gives you the tools to slowly confront things related to the trauma, identify the things that you're avoiding, and finally, how to slowly and effectively face your fears one item at a time. Hopefully, with continuous effort, you'll learn that there's no need for avoidance because the trauma-related memories and triggers do not pose any real danger to you in the present.

Eye Movement Desensitization and Reprocessing Therapy (EMDR)

Eye Movement Desensitization and Reprocessing Therapy (EMDR) is made up of a set of structured protocols and procedures that are based on the adaptive information processing (AIP) model (how your brain stores memories).[11]

During therapy, you will be asked to think or talk about the trauma you experienced or witnessed while moving your eyes in response to stimuli in the room. The general idea is that EMDR helps your brain *reprocess* how the event has affected you emotionally.

If you remember, involuntary Re-Experiencing (page 23) is one of the major symptoms of PTSD. When things are normal, your brain captures memories smoothly and links them together to remind you of other things.

For example, say you had a great family vacation to Disneyland when you were a kid, and that first night you had “the best burger ever!”. Today, you recall that happy memory whenever you eat the same burger. But even though you remember that memory, you know it happened years ago. You smile and move on.

During a traumatic event, that brain networking doesn't function as it should. The brain can go “offline,” and there is a gap between what you feel, hear, and see and what your language-based memory stores. There’s a sort of involuntary time loop.

For example, say you and your friend were victims of a robbery. When this occurred, you were in a dark alley, and your friend got stabbed and killed. Months or years later, you’re out with some friends and find yourself walking down a dark path. All of a sudden, you break into a sweat. You can hardly breathe and feel very afraid. You’re involuntarily re-experiencing the trauma. Your brain is not telling you that the danger is over, and it has been for some time now.

The goal of EMDR is to help your brain reprocess what you remember from the traumatic incident (through rhythmic eye movements). And in doing so, repair the mental injury you suffered from the trauma so that involuntary re-experiencing happens less (or not at all).

Dialectical Behavior Therapy (DBT)

And, of course, there’s Dialectical Behavior Therapy or DBT, which we will cover in great detail in Chapter 3.

A note about medication: There are medications prescribed for PTSD, usually antidepressants. When used to treat PTSD, they work to lessen PTSD symptoms. I believe that if you’re not suffering from any other underlying mental health condition, such as depression, trauma-focused psychological treatment should be the first option. Please consult a doctor regarding the option that's best for you.

Are you showing a normal stress response to a traumatic experience or is it PTSD? For clarity, you can go over the PTSD Self-Evaluation exercise on *Appendix B (page 147).*

Chapter Highlights:

- TRAUMA is at the core of PTSD.
- Stress is a normal response to trauma. PTSD is when normal stress turns into *distress* or *chronic stress* that gets in the way of your daily life.
- People with PTSD are not just war veterans but anyone who has experienced or witnessed a traumatic event.
- PTSD Symptoms: intrusive symptoms, avoidance symptoms, negative changes in mood and thoughts, and hyper-reactivity (being on edge).
- PTSD Types: uncomplicated PTSD, dissociative PTSD, complex PTSD and comorbid PTSD.
- PTSD treatments: Cognitive Behavioral Therapy (CBT), Prolonged Exposure Therapy (PET), Eye Movement Desensitization and Reprocessing Therapy (EMDR), and Dialectic Behavior Therapy (DBT).

Chapter 2: Living with PTSD

"It isn't in my past. It's in my every day." – Helen Wilson

According to the National Center for PTSD of the US Department of Veterans Affairs, *"about 6 of every 10 men (or 60%) and 5 of every 10 women (or 50%) experience at least one trauma in their lives"*. Women are more likely to be sexually assaulted or sexually abused as a child, while men are more likely to be involved in accidents, physical assaults, battles, natural disasters, or witness deaths or injuries.[12] Globally, 3.9% of the population has PTSD.[13]

Despite the above already concerning statistics, **PTSD is considered one of the most undiagnosed disorders**.[14,15,16] That's not surprising since Avoidance (page 23) is one of its symptoms. In my personal experience, *cultural norms* play a role too.

Content Warning: the following story contains potentially distressing material.

Here's my mom's story: My mom had a very difficult childhood growing up. However, talking about such things is not in Chinese culture. But when I was a kid, my mom would often experience nightmares. The silence of the night would be pierced by her screams, which were so loud that I would wake up in my room down the hall. This didn't happen every night, but it went on for years.

When I was older, I finally mustered up the courage to ask her why she thought she had these nightmares. She said she didn't know. When I asked her if something terrible happened when she was a kid, she said, *"Well, when I was six or seven, a pot of boiling water accidentally tipped over and poured all over me."*

I stared at my mom in disbelief and asked her what had happened afterward. *How badly was she burned? Did anyone bring her to the doctor? How long did it take her to heal?* She said she didn't remember that part. I wanted to know more, but my mom didn't like to discuss it further, and that was that.

She has never gone through any therapy, and I doubt she ever will because mental health was, and still is, very much a taboo in Chinese culture.

How PTSD Affects Your Brain

PTSD affects brain function.[17] Specifically, it affects our brain's *context processing* abilities, which is our ability to recognize that a particular stimulus may call for various reactions depending on its context.

For example, suppose the trauma you experienced involved a gunshot. In that case, sounds such as a door banging or fireworks might trigger intense fear even though you are in no danger. Your brain does not take into context that you are in a safe environment now.

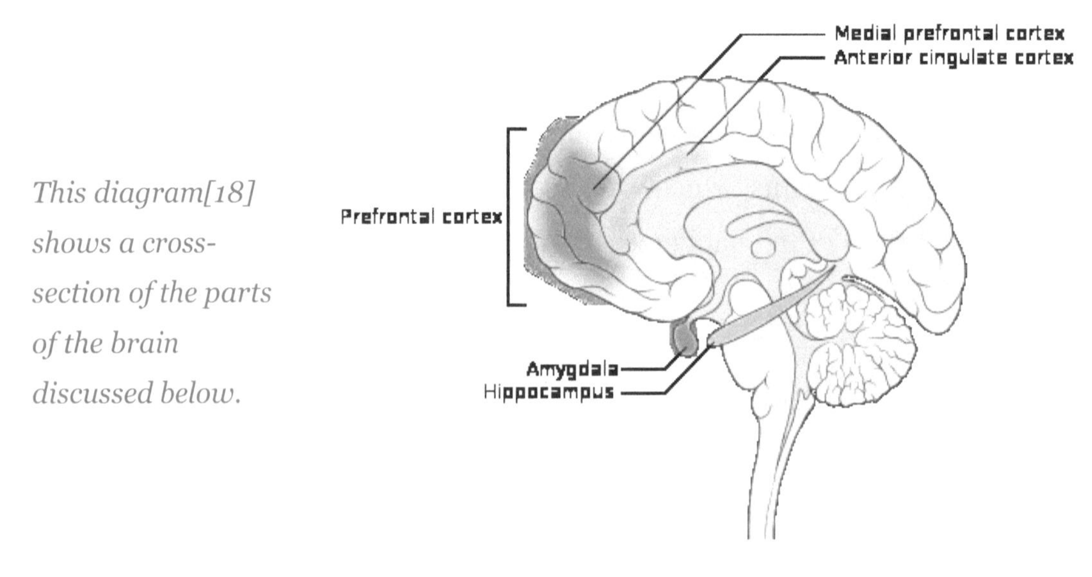

This diagram[18] shows a cross-section of the parts of the brain discussed below.

Amygdala – Your Alarm System

The **amygdala** is an almond-shaped structure in the middle of the brain that helps control our emotions (how we feel) and behavior (how we act). Under normal circumstances, the amygdala processes frightening or threatening stimuli and instructs our brains and bodies on how to respond. For this reason, the amygdala is considered our natural alarm system.

The amygdala in people with PTSD is overstimulated, and it has trouble distinguishing between a threat *then* and a threat *now*.[19] So, when frightening or threatening stimuli are encountered, we overreact so that even common or normal triggers, such as door banging, can send us into a complete panic.

Hippocampus – Your Memory Center

The **hippocampus** is the brain's memory center. As previously mentioned in this book (AIP, page 28), our brains capture memories smoothly when all's well. The hippocampus should be able to recall a traumatic incident and make sense of it afterward.

However, the trauma is so overpowering during a traumatic event that the hippocampus does not store and properly categorize all the information. In fact, research shows that the hippocampus is smaller and less active in people who've experienced trauma.[20]

This implies that because your hippocampus is working so hard to make sense of things, you might have problems recalling crucial parts of the incident (memory loss), or you might find yourself thinking a lot about what happened. (Hence, the involuntary re-living or re-experiencing of the event.)

Prefrontal Cortex – Your Learning Center

The **prefrontal cortex** aids in decision-making and mental observation. When presented with frightening or threatening stimuli, the prefrontal cortex helps us evaluate what's going on and, if necessary, stops us from our emotional urges or impulses.

Research shows that the prefrontal cortex in people with PTSD underperforms.[21] For example, when we hear loud fireworks, and the amygdala (*alarm system*) triggers feelings of fear, the prefrontal cortex cannot always evaluate that there is no danger.

This indicates that people with PTSD are in a never-ending cycle of stress. And as long as the cycle continues, your pain and suffering will too.

How PTSD Affects Your Life

"Even if you've accumulated a house full of nice things and the picture of your life fits inside a beautiful frame, if you have experienced trauma but haven't excavated it, the wounded parts of you will affect everything you've managed to build."
– Oprah Winfrey

PTSD needs to be addressed because it affects all parts of your life. Here are some ways PTSD can hurt you in the long run if you don't take steps to heal or get help.

Tired, just tired. When your brain uses so much energy to protect you from perceived danger and threats, you might feel totally depleted of energy. Initially, you might lack the energy to do daily tasks, but this can progress to self-neglect and self-harming thoughts.

Low self-esteem. Many people who show PTSD symptoms find it hard to seek help. So one of the most damaging things that can happen is to reach out to someone you know only to be invalidated.

Content Warning: the following story contains potentially distressing material.

This is what Nicko**, a reader, had to say: *"I won't go into details about what I saw, heard, and did during the war, but I was a 26-year-old war vet when I first tried to reach out to someone. This person told me, "What did you expect? You're a soldier. You knew what you signed up for." Since I trusted this person, their reaction made me question if I was overreacting or maybe I was just not "man enough."*

This made me want to keep what I was going through a secret. The years went by, and things just got worse for me. My sleeping problems worsened, and I turned to alcohol. At one point, I was in a relationship and tried to tell her about it, but then she said, "That was YEARS ago. Don't hide being an alcoholic to this PTSD."

I can't tell you how much it took from me just to try and talk to someone. The fact that I wasn't taken seriously bothers me to this day."

(**Note**: Nicko met Anna** in 2014 in an AA meeting. She was the one who finally listened and encouraged Nicko to join her and try DBT.)

Please note that *invalidating* and *gaslighting* are not the same, but they are both very damaging.[22,23] Invalidating is when someone tells you that you shouldn't feel what you're feeling. Gaslighting is when someone is trying to convince you that you don't actually feel that way. People who invalidate or gaslight you make you question yourself, which harms your self-esteem. In addition, it delays you from seeking treatment for your PTSD.

Broken relationships. Trauma can make you distrustful of others and overprotective of yourself. Since trust is an issue, closeness also becomes a

---

** *Names changed for privacy.*

problem. You might have difficulties communicating or connecting with others and may even begin to self-isolate. Unfortunately, the painful opposite is also true. That is, if others don't understand, can't connect, or can't sympathize with you, they might avoid or leave you.

Psychological problems. Humans are not meant to be alone. We thrive when we can share this journey called life. However, PTSD promotes loneliness, which is linked to various mental health problems, such as depression and anxiety.[24,25,26] With increased isolation, other issues such as substance abuse, alcoholism, self-harm, intermittent explosive disorder (impulsive and violent anger), suicidal thoughts[27,28], and others may develop.

Physiological problems. You've heard this before: stress can kill you. Actually, "everyday stress" or "normal stress" does not kill you, but chronic stress does. Studies show that PTSD can cause many physical health problems, such as obesity, diabetes, heart disease, autoimmune disease, etc.[29]

Financial problems. When PTSD interferes with your capacity to do daily tasks, this can negatively affect your employment (potential job loss). Another symptom of PTSD is engaging in self-destructive or risky behavior. This might cause you to make bad financial decisions such as gambling, entering bad investments, etc.

There are many other ways that PTSD can negatively affect your life. You can develop sleep disorders, eating disorders, lack of peace of mind, lack of life enjoyment, etc. In my journey, I've come to think of these negative consequences as "costs."

For example, my OCD and GAD led to my depression (*mental costs*). My loneliness led to my low self-esteem, which made it very hard for me to have and keep relationships (*social costs*). My way of coping was to engage in unhealthy eating, which led me to gain weight and develop a weakened immune system (*physical costs*).

One day, after another night of restless sleep, I opened my eyes and stared at the ceiling. I had absolutely ZERO energy and enthusiasm for the day ahead. And then, a thought popped into my head—*"Life can be better, right?"*

One thought. One sentence. One wish. That's what started my mental healing journey. And in the next chapter, I'll share with you what worked for me. It's my sincere hope that it works for you too.

Chapter Highlights:

- About 6 of every 10 men (or 60%) and 5 of every 10 women (or 50%) experience at least one trauma in their lives.
- PTSD is one of the most misunderstood or undiagnosed mental health disorders.
- PTSD changes how certain parts of our brains function, sending us into a never-ending cycle of stress.
- PTSD affects every aspect of our lives (mentally, socially, physically, financially, emotionally, etc.)

Chapter 3: What is Dialectical Behavior Therapy?

"Life is very interesting, because in the end, some of your greatest pains become your greatest strengths."
- Drew Barrymore

DBT History

Dialectical Behavior Therapy, or **DBT**, was created by Dr. Marsha Linehan[30], Ph.D., in the 1980s. It was initially meant to treat people with borderline personality disorder (BPD). This mental health condition makes it hard for people to control their emotions.

DBT is a variation of Cognitive Behavioral Therapy (CBT). However, while CBT focuses on discovering a client's unhealthy thinking patterns and changing them into positive ones (*change-focused*), Dr. Linehan believes it's more effective to apply two opposing (*dialectical*) concepts instead: **Acceptance** AND **Change**.

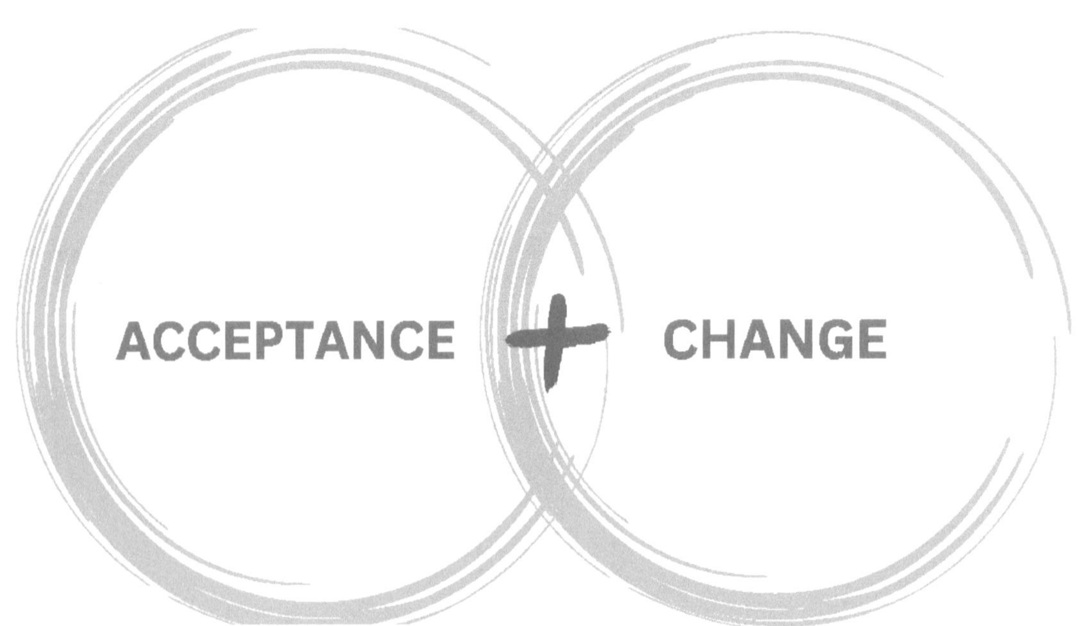

DBT proposes that before a person can start to heal, they should first accept the reality of their situation. Dr. Linehan's personal story[31] underlines this belief.

In the 1960s, Dr. Linehan, then only 17 years old, was admitted into the *Institute of Living*, a psychiatric facility for her "extreme social withdrawal." While at the clinic, she engaged in self-harming activities and displayed suicidal behavior, so she was kept in isolation for her own safety.

Dr. Linehan believed that she had *bipolar disorder* (BPD) then, but since the illness was not yet known in the 1960s, she was misdiagnosed with *schizophrenia*. She was subjected to electroconvulsive therapy for this illness and given Thorazine and Librium as treatment. However, since she did NOT have schizophrenia, these methods did not work to alleviate her mental health problems.

After more than two years, Dr. Linehan was released from the clinic, but she was far from well. It would be another four years before she would have an epiphany about her mental health.

Dr. Linehan says that she was praying at church when she started to think that her suicide attempts were because the gap between *who she was* and *who she wanted to be* was so big that it made her feel hopeless and desperate. She wanted a better life but didn't know how to get it. This was when she realized that she needed to do more than focus on CHANGE.

Yes, CHANGE is necessary for growth and happiness, but ACCEPTANCE is the first step down that road.

Dr. Linehan realized that she had to accept her reality "as is" before moving on. Even though her emotions, behavior, and actions were destructive, they made sense because she was so unhappy and suffering from her present reality. Dr. Linehan would eventually call this concept **Radical Acceptance**.

Radical Acceptance is when you acknowledge the facts of your reality, whatever they may be. You don't need to dissect, evaluate, judge, fight, or even react.

So, Radical Acceptance is accepting your reality; now what? This brings us to the second concept of DBT—**Change**.

You have this book in your hands because you want to feel better. You want your situation to be better so that you can go on and live a better life. Change is what makes that happen.

For example, say you're in a room with the door closed. Outside the room is a small gathering of your family and friends. You can hear them having a great time over there. They sound happy, and you believe joining them will make you happy too. But they will not go into your room and bring the party to you. So, what do you do?

Radical Acceptance = I'm unhappy in this room. The door is locked.
Change = Get up, open the door, walk out, and join the party.

DBT Concepts: Radical Acceptance and Desire to Change

Dialectic means looking at things from more than one point of view. In DBT, it means the fusion of two seemingly opposing concepts: **Acceptance** and **Change**.

At first glance, it might seem unclear. How can you *accept* and *change* at the same time? But you see, you're not accepting and changing the same thing.

What you are accepting is the reality of your current situation. You're also accepting your emotions regarding the situation. What you're changing is your normal reaction to that situation.

Why do I need to practice Radical Acceptance? It's essential to accept the reality of your situation because if you don't, you're ignoring or denying it. And doing this *prolongs your suffering*. You cannot change something you cannot accept.

Imagine being in a maze. If you ignore or deny that you're in it, you stay inside that maze. However, if you accept reality (*I'm in a maze*), you can proceed to the next step—getting out of it.

When you're radically accepting, remember that you should do it without judgment. Do your best to free the mind of your own opinions. You're in a maze. That's it for now.

RADICAL ACCEPTANCE = IT IS WHAT IT IS

Why do I need to change? Because whatever you're doing, they're not working for you. Let's go back to our maze example.

> *David is in a maze, and he doesn't like it! He's angry, and when David's furious, he lashes out, so he starts clenching his fists, breathes rapidly, shouts, and walks in any direction. After 10 minutes, David is STILL in the maze and even angrier.*
>
> *George is in a maze, and he's filled with dread. He can't stand confined spaces, and he's stressing out. He's sweating bullets, clenching his teeth, and breathing rapidly. George is panicking and is frozen in place. He can't seem to take a single step or move a muscle. After a few minutes, George is STILL in the maze, and his anxiety levels are higher.*

The above examples illustrate that reacting to one's emotional impulses (i.e., doing what you would typically do) does not improve the situation.

For David, learning how to control his anger instead of reacting to it gives him a better chance of getting out of the maze sooner. For George, learning to manage his distress instead of acting according to it gives him a better chance of getting out of the maze sooner.

And there's another layer here: by learning new behaviors, you avoid suffering from the weight of your unpleasant emotions. For me, this is one of the most essential lessons in DBT.

Here's how I applied **Acceptance** and **Change** in my life: As mentioned, my teen years were filled with loneliness. I didn't want to accept the reality of my situation (having zero friends) because, in my mind, that meant admitting I wasn't loveable or likable in any way or that I really didn't belong in our new environment. My response to this was to self-isolate. It was my way of protecting my ego and my feelings. But that way of dealing with things meant I never went out and met anyone, which worsened my loneliness, low self-esteem, and depression. I was caught in a dark, vicious cycle of my own undoing.

I discovered DBT as an adult, so I cannot go back and rewrite my teen years. (Believe me, I wish I could.) However, I can make my adult years better.

So, as painful and challenging as it was, I accepted the reality of my situation: I still had no real friends, was very lonely, and felt empty. I felt invisible, too, as if I was walking around and no one saw or heard me. It hurts to live like this.

Now, the "old me" would react by self-isolating as usual. But that wouldn't work. It never did, so why would it work now, right? So, I changed. I learned new behaviors to get a different outcome.

"Your life does not get better by chance;
it gets better by change." – Jim Rohn

I wish I could tell you that things got better overnight. It didn't. Change takes time—but it's time well spent.

But HOW does one change? Ah, that's the real question. How do you get from A to Z? Well, that's one of the many things I like about dialectical behavior therapy. It's not just theory. DBT gave me the "HOW" I needed to change.

DBT Worksheets in this Book

We learn when we apply what we know in what we do (knowledge + action). So, this book not only talks about the DBT principles but also gives you worksheets to help you put these principles into action in your own life. Many of these exercises are adapted from Dr. Linehan's *DBT Skills Training Manual*[32], while the rest are ones I've found helpful when practicing DBT skills.

When doing these exercises for the first time, I recommend you do them in a place you feel safe, comfortable, and unlikely to be disturbed.

Lastly, I encourage you to keep doing the exercises until the DBT way of feeling, thinking, and behaving becomes natural. Also, if there are any exercises or worksheets you're not ready to do, that's okay. You can always go back to then when you're ready.

Worksheet: Radical Acceptance

Radical Acceptance is reality acceptance. So, for your first exercise, please write down inside the circle below what your reality is right now. Write down whatever comes to your mind. Try not to judge your situation. Imagine your current situation as if you're watching a movie and just taking notes.

Examples: (1) I'm in pain. (2) I'm tired. (3) People confuse me. (4) Loud noises scare me. (5) I am not okay.

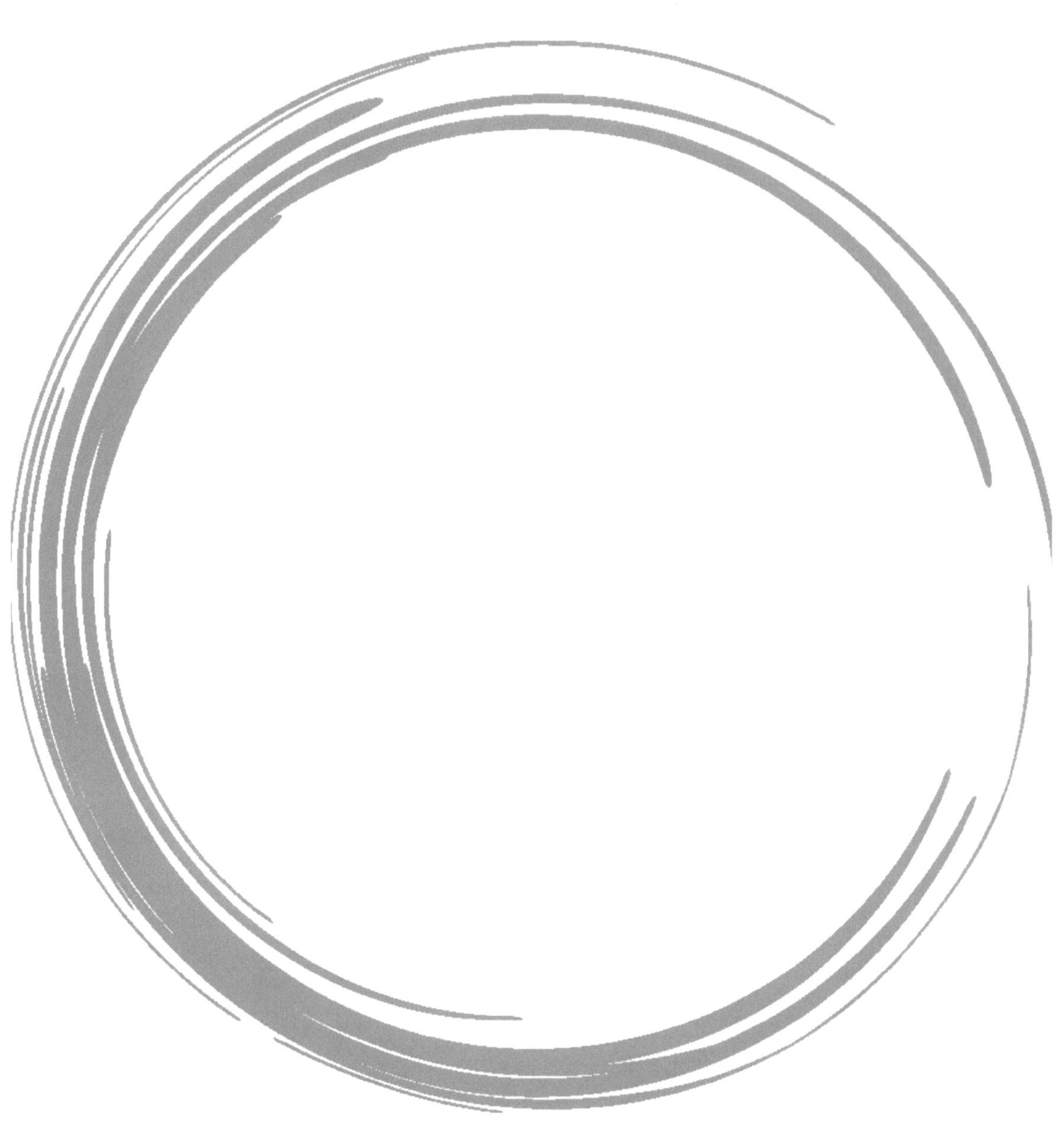

Worksheet: Desire to Change

Set yourself up to welcome change in your life. You don't need to make any plans here. Just be kind to yourself and imagine why change can benefit you. Write down whatever comes to your mind inside the circle below.

Examples: (1) I'm open to change. (2) I'm ready for "new." (3) I'm ready for "better." (4) I know I can be happier. (5) It's time for "more."

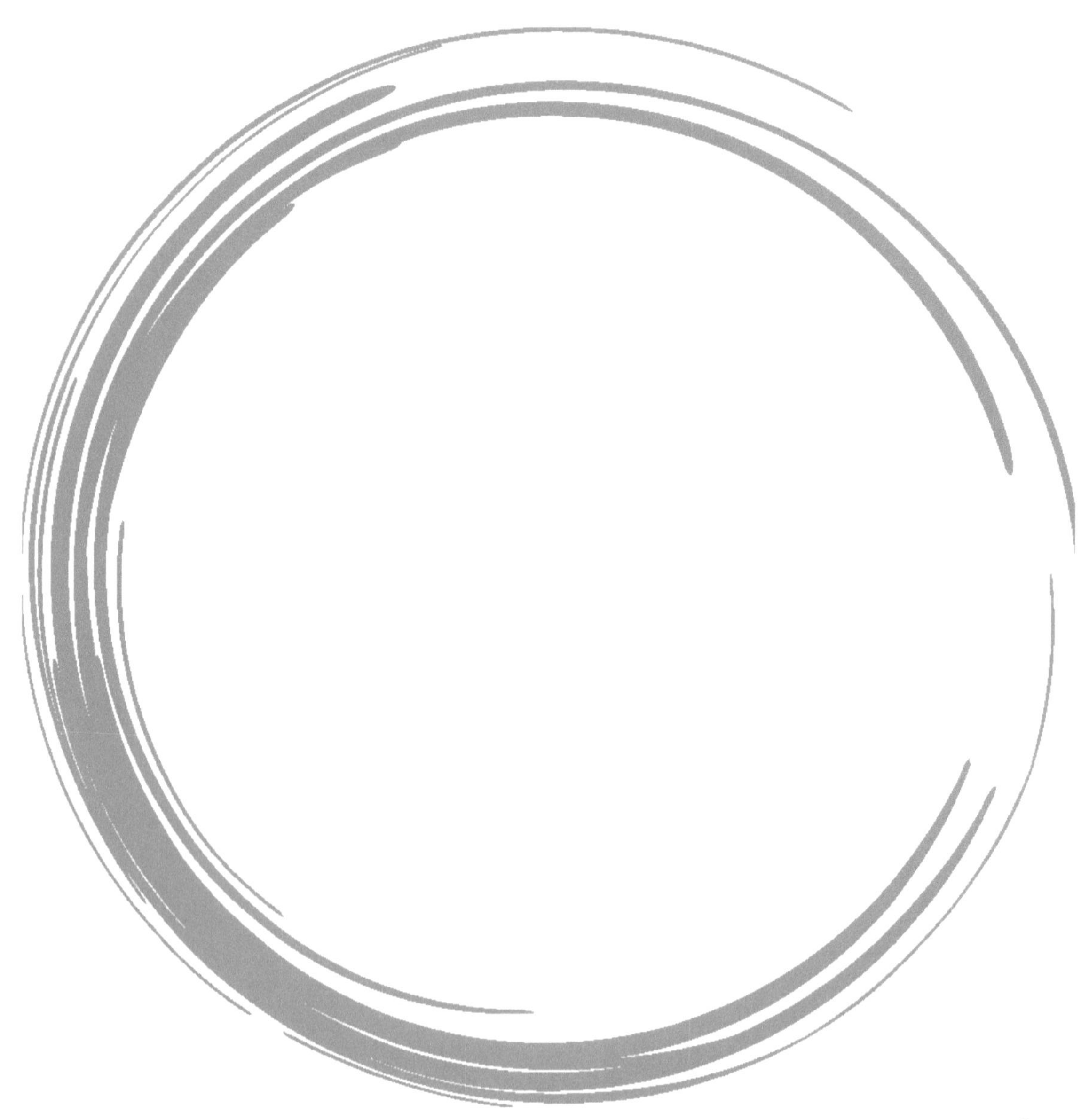

Worksheet: Acceptance + Change

Now, let's complete the picture. Under Radical Acceptance and Desire to Change, copy what you wrote in the previous exercises. In the middle, write down a Statement for yourself. Acknowledge today and what you want for tomorrow.

Here's an example:

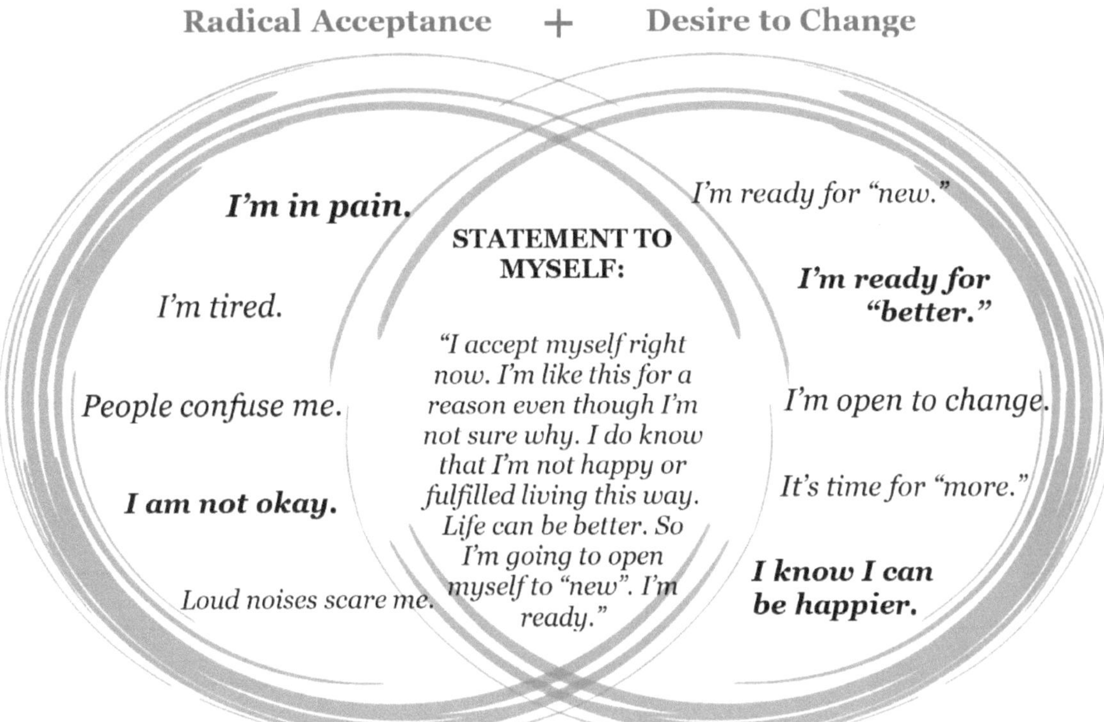

It's your turn on the next page:

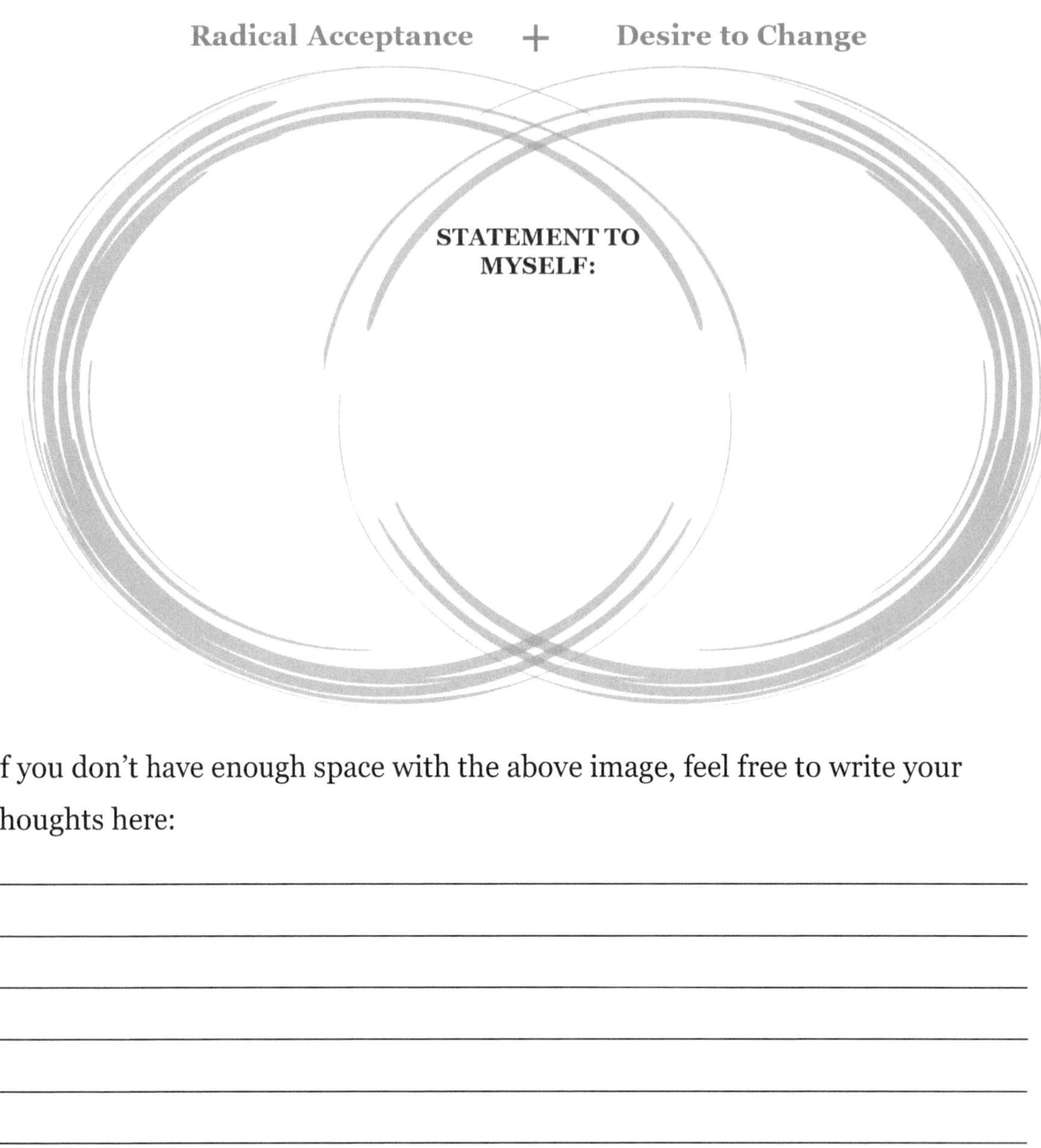

If you don't have enough space with the above image, feel free to write your thoughts here:

DBT Core Skills

Adopting **Acceptance** and **Change** in your life requires practicing four primary skills: *Mindfulness*, *Distress Tolerance*, *Emotion Regulation,* and *Interpersonal Effectiveness*.

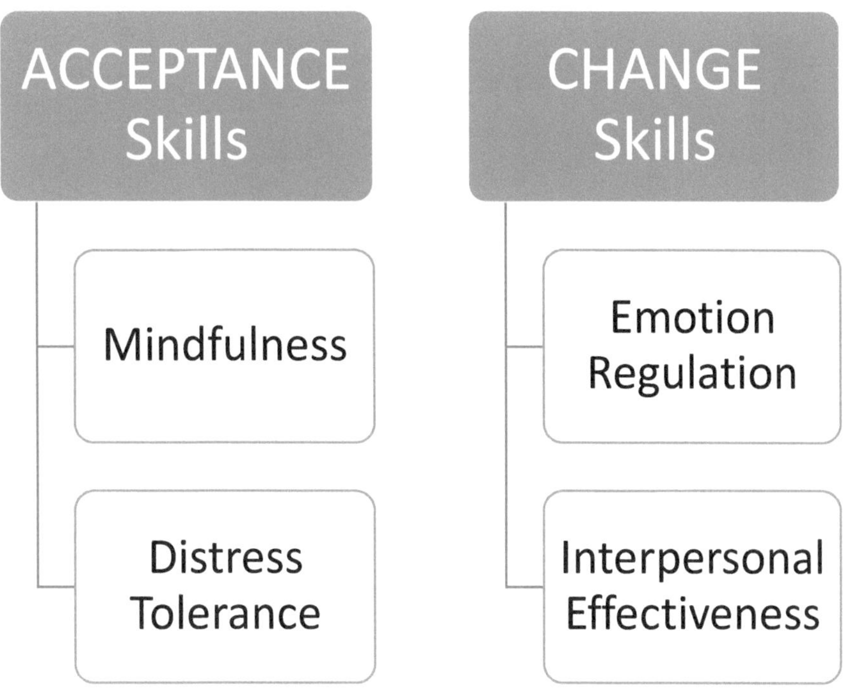

As the image above shows, Acceptance is possible by learning *Mindfulness* and *Distress Tolerance* skills. At the same time, Change takes place by learning *Emotion Regulation* and *Interpersonal Effectiveness* skills.

Mindfulness

What comes to your mind when you hear the word "mindfulness"? You're probably picturing someone meditating on a mat with their eyes closed, hands gently clasped, and legs crossed. However, there's a BIG difference between the two: mindfulness is a way of being (*who you are*), while meditation is a practice (*what you do*).

Mindfulness is a state of awareness or being fully present in NOW. Meditation is a technique to help you achieve mindfulness.

But how does one become mindful? In DBT, this is achieved by learning **WHAT** and **HOW** skills.

WHAT **Skills**

These skills are about **WHAT we have to do** to be mindful.

- **Observe.** Pay attention to what's happening inside and around you. Open your eyes and your senses entirely to whatever you're experiencing.

  For example, when was the last time you really paid attention to eating a meal? Eating is so basic, normal, and routine that most of us don't really give food or how we eat much attention. So, for your next meal, take the time to observe yourself and your food a bit more closely.

  Here are a few things to which you may want to pay attention:
  After a spoonful, what's the first thing you taste (sweetness, sourness, saltiness, bitterness, or savoriness)?
  What are the different textures you feel in your mouth as you chew?
  How often do you take a sip of something to drink while eating?

- **Describe**. Define or discuss what you observe. Often, we're in such a hurry living our lives that we gloss over what's happening around us. One way to "slow down" is to take the time to describe what we observe.

  For example, say you're eating dinner. Describe the scenario. Are you sitting down? If so, describe the chair. Is it new or old? Is there a glass of water next to you? Who put it there? Do you always drink water during a meal? What are you eating? Did you make it? Is it a favorite of yours? Why or why not?

- **Participate**. You get the most out of an experience when participating fully. You're probably not even aware of it anymore, but you do A LOT of things at once.

  For example, what else do you do while eating? Are you on your phone? Are you watching TV? Are you reading something? When was the last time you JUST ate a meal?! You miss so much when you multi-task and don't participate fully in the moment.

HOW Skills

These skills focus on **HOW to be more mindful** in our everyday lives.

- **Non-Judgmentally.** When mindful of something, we don't need to express our opinion. Just observe and describe but don't label anything as "good" or "bad."

  For example, you're mindful that it's raining hard outside. That's it—no need to state how it might ruin your plans for the day.

- **One-Mindfully.** When practicing mindfulness, focus on one thing and one thing only because mental multi-tasking divides awareness.

  For example, you're mindful that it's raining hard outside. Stay with the rain. Watch it fall on the ground and splash brilliantly. Watch it hit the window pane and glide against the glass. Close your eyes and listen. What music is the rain playing for you?

- **Effectively.** Whatever you are mindful of, you are a part of it, so you must participate effectively. Doing so will enable you to get the results you want out of the situation.

  For example, you're working from home and must turn in a report at the end of the day. However, your partner is going in and out of your home office, trying to discuss weekend plans with the kids. You're mindful (aware) of your growing stress and annoyance. However, losing your cool and shouting will lead to an argument (less time to do your report), which can ruin your weekend (more stress you don't need). In this situation, it's far more effective to say something like, *"I hear you, honey, but give me an hour to finish this first. You'll have my full attention then."*

Mindfulness is not just a switch we turn "On," especially today when many things entice and demand our attention. Also, when we're tired, sad, exhausted, hungry, running late, etc., it's hard to be mindful—but it's not impossible.

Like most things we want to master, mindfulness needs practice, practice, practice!

Worksheet: Box Breathing

This deep breathing exercise is a great way to practice mindfulness. It will help limit your focus and allow you to be in the here and now. Another benefit to Box Breathing, also known as *four-square breathing*, is that you can do it anywhere.

1. Sit up straight on a chair, lie on a mat or on your bed, or stand, whatever is most comfortable for you.
2. Breathe in deeply for a count of four (4).
   Mentally count 4-3-2-1.
3. Hold your breath for a count of four (4).
   Mentally count 4-3-2-1.
4. Exhale for a count of four (4).
   Mentally count 4-3-2-1.
5. Hold your breath for a count of four (4).
   Mentally count 4-3-2-1.
6. Do this for at least five rounds or cycles.

Worksheet: A Mindfulness Habit

This exercise will help you practice Mindfulness **WHAT** and **HOW** skills.

Tip: This exercise is best done when you're alone and not likely to be interrupted.

- Get some "ME" time and choose any of these activities.
  - Coffee/tea break.
  - Take a leisurely walk.
  - Walk your pet.
  - Sit in nature.
  - Take a bath.
  - Listen to music.
  - Others:

    ____

    ____

    ____

- Next, fill out this Mindfulness table. If one aspect does not apply to what you're doing, just write some notes about it, but DO NOT leave it blank. I've done one for you as an example.

ME Time Activity: *Coffee break.* **Time you started:** *4:15 PM*	
Observe. *Use your senses (eyes, nose, ears, hands, and tongue). Don't describe anything. Just focus and pay attention to what your senses are picking up.* • *I'm looking at the coffee.* • *Smelling the coffee.* • *I'm putting my hands around the mug.* • *I just took a sip of the coffee.*	**Non-Judgmentally.** *Free your mind of any opinions. Nothing is good or bad. Nothing is right or wrong. Just state facts.* *When I first smelled the coffee, I immediately thought, "this smells strong; I won't like it." I had to smell it again and focus on the scent itself.*

ME Time Activity: *Coffee break.* **Time you started:** *4:15 PM*	
Describe. *Put into words what you've observed.* • *Sight: it's a very dark color; coffee is swirling; I still see smoke* • *Smell: deep aroma* • *Touch: the mug's really warm to touch* • *Taste: dark, almost bitter*	**One-Mindfully.** *Pull yourself back to NOW and your selected activity whenever your mind wanders.* *Wow, how the mind wanders! To re-focus, I would trace the mug's rim with my fingers to bring me back to just drinking coffee.*
Participate. *How are you engaging with this activity?* *I'm sitting alone in the dining room. I didn't turn on any music or anything to distract me. I left my mobile phone (on Silent!) in another room.*	**Effectively.** *What is your goal with this activity? Ask yourself if you're achieving it. (If not, you're not engaging in it effectively.)* ***Goal****: Practice mindfulness; stop my mind from thinking about a dozen different things for a while.* ***Am I achieving it?*** *Yeah, I think I am. It's been eight minutes, and I'm still here. Just me and my coffee.*

Your Turn:

ME Time Activity: **Time you started:**	
Observe. *Use your senses (eyes, nose, ears, hands, and tongue). Don't describe anything. Just focus and pay attention to what your senses are picking up.*	**Non-Judgmentally.** *Free your mind of any opinions. Nothing is good or bad. Nothing is right or wrong. Just state facts.*
Describe. *Put into words what you've observed.*	**One-Mindfully.** *Pull yourself back to NOW and your selected activity whenever your mind wanders.*
Participate. *How are you engaging with this activity?*	**Effectively.** *What is your goal with this activity? Ask yourself if you're achieving it. (If not, you're not engaging in it effectively.)* ***Goal***: ***Am I achieving it?***

Self-Analysis:

1. After doing your "ME" time activity, rate your Mindfulness level from 1-10, with 1 being completely unable to focus on your activity and 10 being easy for you to 100% concentrate on what you're doing. Mark or encircle your answer.

1	2	3	4	5	6	7	8	9	10

In all likelihood, you'll find it challenging to practice Mindfulness at first; that's okay. That's normal. I promise that you WILL get better at it with constant practice. So I suggest you do this exercise at least once a week, choosing whatever activity you want and noting your progress.

2. Which Mindfulness skill were you having the most difficulty with? Mark or encircle your answer.

Observe	Non-Judgmentally
Describe	One Mindfully
Participate	Effectively

Spend a few extra minutes on the skill you need to work on the next time you do this exercise.

For example, if you consistently offer an opinion (judgment) about something, re-focus and keep trying to state only FACTS.

Distress Tolerance

Stress is a natural response to anything that we deem unpleasant, and it's not always a bad thing. For example, if you're starting a new job, stress can help you focus, drive you to do well at work, and improve your performance.

Eustress is stress that is positive or constructive. It's the type of stress that pushes you just enough outside your comfort zone to be beneficial in the end. For example, if you're stressed about traveling to a new country, doing it anyway will most likely result in a positive experience. (New places, new people, and new experiences help you grow as a person.[33,34])

Distress is stress that is negative or harmful. It's the type of stress that's crippling and makes you feel unable to cope with a situation. Chronic distress can damage your self-esteem and harm your physical and mental health.[35]

Eustress and distress: what's the difference? One way to differentiate between the two is to evaluate events in terms of "challenges" or "threats."[36] If you view something as a "challenge," there's this belief in you that no matter how difficult it is, you can overcome it and that the experience, good or bad, will benefit you. If you perceive an event as a "threat," you feel unsafe, and the situation is harmful to you. You might feel overwhelmed and anxious so that you cannot respond (feel, think, or act) appropriately to the event.

With PTSD, you may perceive everything as a threat. In that case, increasing your Distress Tolerance levels is your first line of deference.

Distress Tolerance is one's ability to withstand psychological discomfort effectively. And people with mental health problems have a *low* distress tolerance level.

When we cannot handle stressful, upsetting, and demanding situations well, we tend to ignore, deny, fight or run away from whatever's causing our distress. The problem with this coping mechanism is that the next time you deal with the same thing—you will be in distress all over again.

This is why **Distress Tolerance** skills are part of **Acceptance** in DBT. This way, you are not ignoring, fighting, denying, or escaping anything. You accept that a situation is distressing. Now, you can start tolerating (surviving) your emotional response (your distress) about it.

Also, when we don't deal with our distress (as it's happening), we might lash out or behave in ways that might make the situation worse. We do this because we want to get the pressure off and feel better immediately.

For example, say you're in a very heated argument with your boss again. People are watching. Your heart is racing, your head is pounding, and you feel overwhelmed. You're starting to see red. If you can't tolerate your distress, you might shout back, throw something, or even shove your boss. But then what? You might lose your job.

Distress Tolerance skills help you accept reality (the situation as it is *in the moment*, not forever) even though you don't like it and endure them without making them worse.

The following exercises are some of the first DBT distress tolerance skills I learned. I still use them today whenever something distresses me. I hope they come to your aid too.

Worksheet: 5-4-3-2-1 Grounding Technique

Grounding techniques help pull you away from distress by bringing your attention to the present. This grounding exercise calls upon your five senses.

Name five (5) things you can see.
Examples: pen, coffee mug, post-it note, sanitizer, speaker

1.
2.
3.
4.
5.

Name four (4) things you can touch.
Examples: keyboard, apple, water bottle, my clothes

1.
2.
3.
4.

Name three (3) things you can hear.
Examples: car, kids, radio

1.
2.
3.

Name two (2) things you can smell.
Examples: coffee, cologne

1.
2.

Name one (1) thing you can taste.
Example: candy

1.

If you're still in distress, try this exercise again or list down AS MANY things as you can per sense.

Worksheet: The Grounding Wheel

When in distress, choose an activity from the **Grounding Wheel** below. Depending on where you are, you may not be able to do some of the activities below, so feel free to make your own **Grounding Wheel** with activities easily accessible to you. *Examples*: *hold my dog and feel its fur, listen to my Spotify "feel good" playlist, grab my journal and list positive things, etc.*

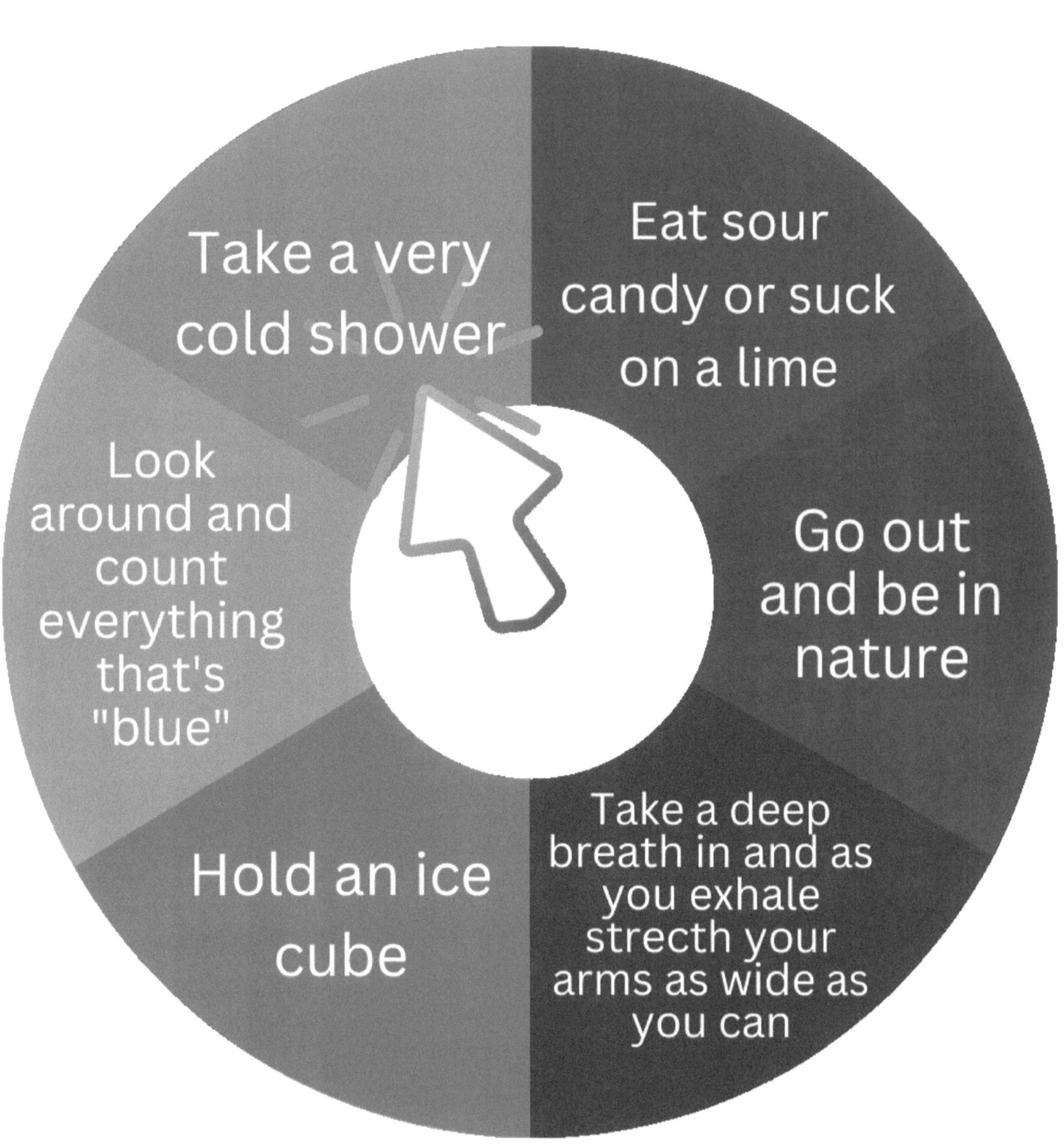

Emotion Regulation

Emotions are reactions to stimuli. According to the *American Psychological Association* (APA), emotions are "a complex reaction pattern involving *experiential, behavioral,* and *physiological* elements."[37]

Experiential Elements

All emotions are prompted. Someone or something is causing the emotional effect. However, the actual emotion produced is based on our personal experiences.

For example, hearing someone sing *Happy Birthday* may prompt happiness *if* they have happy memories of their childhood or birthdays. In contrast, if a loved one suddenly passes away during their birthday, hearing the song might trigger feelings of sadness or even anger.

Behavioral Elements

The actual expression of emotion is the behavioral component of an emotional response. Several factors influence this element, such as our upbringing, individual personalities, cultural norms, and others.

For example, it always amazes me how easy it is for some people to say *"I love you"* or give hugs when they're happy. This is not the norm in *my* family. I didn't grow up with such free expressions of love and happiness, so this is not a behavior I would regularly show.

Physiological Elements

How our body reacts to the emotion we feel is the physiological element of an emotional response. Our autonomic nervous system (ANS) responds when an emotion is triggered. The ANS controls involuntary body responses, such as heart rate, blood flow, respiration, and digestion. A branch of the ANS is the sympathetic nervous system (SNS), which controls our fight-or-flight response.

However, the ANS and the SNS are not the only things that control our bodies' reactions to emotions. Studies show that the amygdala also plays a vital role in our emotional responses. (If you remember, we discussed that the amygdala in people with PTSD is overstimulated (page 33), making it one of the reasons why people appear to be constantly "on edge" and overact to stimuli.)

So this is the process of emotions: there's a prompting event, and based on our personal experiences (*subjective experience*), an emotional response is produced. Our bodies react to the emotion we're feeling (*physiological response*), and we show this emotion externally through our behavior (*behavioral response*).

Now, what does this have to do with our mental health? **When we struggle to manage or regulate painful emotions such as sadness, anger, fear, and disgust, we are more likely to engage in dysfunctional behavior.** And when we act this way, we harm ourselves the most.

Content Warning: the following story contains potentially distressing material.

This is what Kris[††], a reader, had to say: *"I was raped when I was 14 by someone I knew at a home party my parents forbade me to attend. I was confused. I was ashamed. I was afraid. I was angry. I was disgusted. And a huge part of me was blaming myself. If only this... if only that... I didn't tell anyone and internalized everything because I couldn't deal with what had happened.*

It would take me a long time to list down all the bad things I did and all the bad decisions I made over the years. So, I'll just say this: when I was 27, I found myself at a rooftop party for the company I was working for. I didn't hear anything around me. All I could think of was walking towards the ledge.

[††] *Name changed for privacy.*

Although I have no recollection of moving, I physically walked towards the ledge because a colleague grabbed my wrist and dragged me inside. She stared at me and asked softly, "Do you need help?" I cried as I had never cried before in my life. I visited a psychiatrist after that and was diagnosed with PTSD.

I'm still seeing my psychiatrist, and she was actually the one who introduced me to DBT. I've learned a lot of important things from DBT that really helped me. I discovered that Acceptance can be very healing. I realized that I was victimizing myself repeatedly because I couldn't manage my painful and disturbing emotions. And although hard to deal with, I learned that I was sort of "suffering by choice" and that I could end that suffering if I wanted and was willing to do the work."

"Pain is inevitable. Suffering is optional."
– Haruki Murakami

In many ways, **Emotion Regulation** is about understanding yourself. It's **awareness of painful emotions and how you can regulate them so that you don't act in destructive ways (**thereby causing or prolonging your suffering).

IMPORTANT: Emotion Regulations skills are NOT about denying or getting rid of emotions. We are human because of our capacity to feel, so we will not judge or invalidate our emotions. The goal is to reduce our vulnerability to unpleasant feelings and to find ways to manage or regulate them effectively.

Your emotions are not who you are. You can (and should) **feel your feelings; just don't act on them all the time**.

Worksheet: Accumulate, Build, Cope (ABC)

This exercise will help you become less sensitive and vulnerable to painful emotions. It will build your resilience so that if and when an unpleasant situation happens, you can cope with it.

Imagine your life as a bucket. If it's filled with pleasant events, then there's not a lot of room left for negative ones. That's what this exercise is all about.

A	Accumulate Positive Emotions
B	Build Mastery
C	Cope Ahead

Accumulate Positive Emotions (Short- and Long-Term)

Short Term: List down **10 positive activities** that bring you joy that you can do today. *Examples: swimming, doing yoga, gardening, etc.*

1. ______________________________
2. ______________________________
3. ______________________________
4. ______________________________
5. ______________________________
6. ______________________________
7. ______________________________
8. ______________________________
9. ______________________________
10. ______________________________

Long Term: List down **10 positive changes** you want to make, so that positive events happen more often in the future. *Examples: stop smoking TO improve my health, start limiting my time on the phone TO be more present in my own life*

1. ______________________ *to* ______________________
2. ______________________ *to* ______________________
3. ______________________ *to* ______________________
4. ______________________ *to* ______________________
5. ______________________ *to* ______________________
6. ______________________ *to* ______________________
7. ______________________ *to* ______________________
8. ______________________ *to* ______________________
9. ______________________ *to* ______________________
10. ______________________ *to* ______________________

Build Mastery

Engage in **activities that make you feel skillful and competent**. Knowing that you're proficient in something is good for your self-esteem and fights feelings of helplessness and hopelessness. *Examples: take online or offline cooking lessons, start CrossFit, etc.*

1. ____
2. ____
3. ____
4. ____
5. ____

Cope Ahead

If you know that certain situations stress you out or trigger unpleasant emotions, create a plan to be ready whenever the event occurs. Whatever your plan is, rehearse it in your mind or roleplay it with someone. This helps you be prepared to do and say what you need to when the time comes.

Stressful Event: ______________________________

Example: mom's birthday

What usually happens? / What are you concerned about?

Example: my oldest brother feels he has achieved the most amongst us siblings and always makes me feel "less." I get furious, which usually ends with me saying or doing something I regret. This, of course, upsets my mom, and I don't particularly appreciate doing that.

____

____

____

____

Plan to cope ahead:

1. Rehearse the situation in your mind.
2. State what you plan to DO. Be as detailed as possible.
   Example:
   - *I will practice Box Breathing (page 53) and go over my Distress Tolerance (page 58) exercises before I go to the party.*
   - *I will sit furthest away from my brother all the time.*
   - *I'll leave the room each time he says something negative about me.*
   - *I'll go to the kitchen when I get angry and hold an ice cube.*

   Your turn:

   ____

   ____

   ____

   ____

   ____

3. State what you plan to SAY. Be as detailed as possible.
   Examples:
   - *Hey dude, I do not appreciate you teasing me. Please stop.*
   - *Hey, how about we give the teasing this year a rest?*
   - *Happy for you. I've got a lot of good stuff going on right now too. (Mention activities I'm doing under* *Build Mastery (page 66).*

   Your turn:

   ____

   ____

   ____

   ____

   ____

Important: When you rehearse your coping ahead strategy, it's normal to experience unpleasant emotions because you are, in effect, recreating the unpleasant situation as if it were happening. As such, it's essential to take a break and relax afterward.

Write down some of the things that make you feel calm right away.

Examples: walking in nature, hugging my dog Lizzie, sitting down and having coffee with my partner, taking a nap

1. ____
2. ____
3. ____
4. ____
5. ____
6. ____
7. ____
8. ____
9. ____
10. ____

Worksheet: PLEASE

This DBT exercise emphasizes how important it is to take care of our physical health because it directly affects our emotional health.[38] If your body is healthy, you're better equipped to regulate your emotions.

PL	Treat Physical Illness
E	Balanced Eating
A	Avoid Unhealthy Substances
S	Quality Sleep
E	Exercise

Following is an explanation of each acronym with some exercises where applicable.

PL Treat Physical Illness

If you're unwell, don't wait to see a physician or refuse to take prescribed medication for your illness. I suggest you also talk to someone (e.g., a friend, a family member, a colleague, etc.) so that you are not alone during this time. If you don't want to see a doctor, then be open to trying a holistic approach to wellness (e.g., reiki, acupuncture, acupressure, etc.). The objective is to GET HELP, so your illness doesn't worsen.

When was the last time you were physically ill?

____

Did you see a doctor? Y / N

Why or why not?

____

____

____

Are you open to alternative therapies? Y / N

If so, which treatment would you like to try?

Examples: reiki, Ayurveda, meditation, yoga, acupuncture, acupressure, aromatherapy, etc.

____

____

____

E Balanced Eating

We are what we eat.[39] The food we consume affects not just how we look but how we feel. As such, eat as close to its natural state as possible because highly processed food has a lot of added sugar, sodium, fat, and chemical preservatives, which harm your health.[40,41] For example, make your own sauce using fresh tomatoes instead of opening a jar or processed pasta sauce.

A **21-day Healthy Swaps** log is provided below. For 21 consecutive days, write down an unhealthy food item (e.g., candy, potato chips) and/or an unhealthy food habit (e.g., skipping breakfast, binge-eating, etc.) that you're replacing with a healthy one. For example, switch to whole-wheat or plant-based pasta instead of consuming white pasta; swap a store-bought processed muffin for a homemade oatmeal cookie, etc.

Tip: Check out sites like *MyFitnessPal* or books like *Eat This, Not That*[42] for advice on achieving a balanced diet.

Why 21 days? In the 1960s, *Dr. Maxwell Maltz*, a plastic surgeon, observed in his book, *Psycho-Cybernetics*[43]that *"[Experiences take] a minimum of about 21 days for an old mental image to dissolve and a new one to jell."* Many studies would prove or disprove this "21 days to form a habit" theory in the succeeding years. Still, in the end, it boils down to what you're trying to do and your determination. For example, giving up chewing gum may be easy for you and require less than 21 days to stick, while wanting to do 30 minutes each day of physical activity will most likely take longer. My opinion is that either way, 21 days is a great way to start.

Note: Please always check with your doctor or a dietitian before making any significant changes in your diet.

21-Day Healthy Swaps

What unhealthy FOOD ITEM are you swapping for a healthy one?
Example: white rice and white bread for brown rice and whole wheat bread

What unhealthy food HABIT are you swapping for a healthy one?
Example: midnight snacking

Were you able to stick to your swap?

Day	Yes	No
Day 1	Y	N
Day 2		
Day 3		
Day 4		
Day 5		
Day 6		
Day 7		

21-Day Healthy Swaps

What unhealthy FOOD ITEM are you swapping for a healthy one?

Example: white rice and white bread for brown rice and whole wheat bread

What unhealthy food HABIT are you swapping for a healthy one?

Example: midnight snacking

Were you able to stick to your swap?

Day	Yes	No
Day 8		
Day 9		
Day 10		
Day 11		
Day 12		
Day 13		
Day 14		

21-Day Healthy Swaps

What unhealthy FOOD ITEM are you swapping for a healthy one?

Example: white rice and white bread for brown rice and whole wheat bread

What unhealthy food HABIT are you swapping for a healthy one?

Example: midnight snacking

Were you able to stick to your swap?

Day	Yes	No
Day 15		
Day 16		
Day 17		
Day 18		
Day 19		
Day 20		
Day 21		

A Avoid Unhealthy Substances

Avoid unhealthy substances like caffeine, alcohol, and illegal drugs as much as possible. According to health experts, adult males need about 15.5 cups of fluids daily. In comparison, females need around 11.5 cups daily, so it's a good idea to switch to drinking water or lemon water. If water is too bland, try green tea or matcha tea. These teas are known for their antioxidant properties, promoting good health.

S Quality Sleep

According to the American Academy of Sleep Medicine (AAS) and Sleep Research Society (SRS), adults need seven (7) or more hours of quality sleep each night regularly.[44] Lack of sleep increases our emotional reactivity and sensitivity to unpleasant stimuli and experiences.[45]

So, are you getting enough sleep? Find out with this **21-Day Sleep Log** below. Every morning write down what time you slept and when you woke up and calculate your total sleep hours.

21-Day Sleep Log			
Day	**Sleep Time**	**Wake Time**	**Total Sleep Hours**
Day 1	*Example: 12 midnight*	*Example: 6 AM*	*Example: 6 hours*
Day 2			
Day 3			
Day 4			
Day 5			
Day 6			
Day 7			
Day 8			
Day 9			
Day 10			
Day 11			
Day 12			

21-Day Sleep Log			
Day	**Sleep Time**	**Wake Time**	**Total Sleep Hours**
Day 13			
Day 14			
Day 15			
Day 16			
Day 17			
Day 18			
Day 19			
Day 20			
Day 21			

Suffering from sleep deprivation? See *Appendix C – Establishing a Sleep Routine (page 151)* *for tips on sleeping faster, better, and longer sleep.*

According to the World Health Organization (WHO), adults aged 18-64 years should engage in at least 150 minutes of moderate-intensity aerobic physical activity (e.g., brisk walking, bike riding, etc.) or at least 75 minutes of vigorous-intensity aerobic physical activity (e.g., jogging, running, swimming laps, etc.), or a combination of both each week.[46] For optimum health, two days of muscle-strengthening activities (e.g., lifting weights, doing push-ups, etc.) should be added per week too.

So, are you moving enough? Find out with this **21-Day Exercise Log** below.

21-Day Exercise Log		
Day	**Exercise Activity**	**Time Spent**
Day 1	*Example: brisk walking*	*Example: 25 mins*
Day 2		
Day 3		
Day 4		
Day 5		
Day 6		
Day 7		
Day 8		
Day 9		
Day 10		
Day 11		
Day 12		
Day 13		
Day 14		

Day 15		
Day 16		
Day 17		
Day 18		
Day 19		
Day 20		
Day 21		

Are you exercising enough? Y / N

If not, make a list of things you can do to do more.

Examples: wake up an hour earlier, park your car as far as possible from work, so you're forced to walk, take the stairs instead of the elevator, make fitness appointments with friends, etc.

I was guilty of not exercising enough too in the beginning. I wanted to increase my daily steps, so I bought a pedometer. After seeing my step count improve, I joined a gym just two blocks from work. The goal is to make exercise an "easy choice" so that it easily fits right into your daily life.

1.
2.
3.
4.

Interpersonal Effectiveness

Relationships are what make life worth living. We are social creatures who want to belong to a unit, want to share what we know, and want to learn from others. Healthy relationships are also critical to our mental and emotional well-being[47,48]. This is because it's not only the good times we want to share. We want to know that when tough times come, we are not alone and have people who will support us.

A great relationship has balance. When there's "give and take," the needs of the people in the relationship are satisfied. So for a relationship to prosper, it's crucial that you:

- Identify your needs and express them;
- Understand the needs of the person in the relationship;
- Know how to communicate your needs; and
- Learn when to compromise to meet the other person's needs.

If one person's needs are met more than the other, then there's an imbalance that can damage the relationship.

Sometimes, though, this imbalance is not intentional. For example, you (or the other person) might not know exactly what you want or need from a relationship. It can also be that you (or the other person) want to stay in the relationship so badly that you compromise your needs. (You never say "No.") In the end, the imbalance always brings dissatisfaction and pain.

Now, it's one thing to KNOW your needs, but it's another to COMMUNICATE them.

For example, when I was in my teens and suffering from extreme loneliness, I knew what I wanted: friends. But whenever I met someone, I didn't know how to start a friendship. I would get all tongue-tied and awkward. (This, of course, would make me self-isolate again, feeding my anxiety and depression.)

So it's these two, identifying needs and effectively communicating them, that's at the heart of **DBT Interpersonal Effectiveness**. When we learn to prioritize ourselves and respect our own wishes while at the same time considering the needs and desires of others, that's when we achieve that relationship balance.

The following exercise is one of the first DBT interpersonal exercises I learned and fully embraced. You see, when I finally got around to identifying my needs and building the courage to speak them out, I would quickly back down the minute I sensed the other person was not inclined to give in to my request.

I didn't want to hear "No," and I didn't like to push because I didn't want the other person to not like me anymore. (All due to my low self-esteem.) I always gave in, which left me empty, angry, and unhappy. The exercise below helped me finally get what I deserve in my relationships.

Worksheet: DEARMAN

This exercise lets you say what you want to say and get what you want to get without harming your relationship. It helps you be more assertive in communicating what you want without being aggressive or inconsiderate.

D	Describe the situation.
E	Express what you want clearly.
A	Be Assertive.
R	Reinforce.
M	Stay Mindful.
A	Appear Confident.
N	Negotiate.

Following is an explanation of each acronym with some exercises for you.

D	Describe the situation.

Before asking, describe the situation first. This way, you and the other person are on the same page regarding the topic. When describing the situation, don't offer opinions or accuse anyone of anything. Be objective and stick to the facts.

Example: You told me you would return home by Friday night, but you didn't.

Your turn:

___

___

E	Express what you want clearly.

When you talk, use "**I**" statements. "**You**" statements can be taken as accusations by the other person, which might turn the conversation into an argument. This is the time when you do convey your emotions and feelings.

Example: I feel taken for granted when you don't bother to tell me where you are. I start to worry about you too.

Your turn:

___

___

A	Be Assertive.

Clearly state what you want (or don't want). Don't assume that the other person knows or "gets it." And even if they do, it's still important to say it yourself.

Example: I would like you to call me if you're not coming home.

Your turn:

___

___

R	Reinforce.

Make sure the other person knows how important your request is. So tell them how grateful you will be if they give you what you want or need.

Example: I would feel much better and not get so worried and stressed if you did that.

Your turn:

___

___

M | Stay Mindful.

Keep your words and feelings in check. Remember that you're in a conversation, so if the other person is not inclined to give in to what you want, they might want to change the subject or start to argue with you. If this happens, control your emotions (feel your feelings, but don't act on them), stay on topic, and maintain your position.

Example: I would still like you to call. I deserve no less.

Your turn:

____

____

A | Appear Confident.

Show your self-assurance through your words and body language. Do not beg or apologize. Also, maintain a consistent demeanor. For instance, do not express what you want confidently and then lower your voice or fidget.

Example: Sit or stand up straight, keep your voice level, maintain eye contact, and then say: I hope you understand where I'm coming from because my stand on this won't change.

Your turn:

____

____

____

____

N	Negotiate.

If the other person is not budging, it's time to negotiate. The goal now is to devise a workable solution to the situation. You can suggest what to do moving forward or ask the other person what they believe should happen next.

Example: How about you send a quick SMS? Surely you can do that.

Your turn:

____

____

Chapter Highlights:

- **Dialectical Behavior Therapy** (DBT) is the practice of two seemingly opposite concepts: **Acceptance** and **Change**.
- There are four (4) primary DBT skills: Mindfulness, Distress Tolerance, Emotion Regulation, and Interpersonal Effectiveness.
- **Mindfulness** is the state of awareness or being fully present in NOW.
- **Distress Tolerance** is about surviving unpleasant, painful situations.
- **Emotion Regulation** is awareness of painful emotions and how to control them so that you don't act in destructive ways (a.k.a. acting on your emotions).
- **Interpersonal Effectiveness** is identifying your needs in a relationship and learning how to ask for them (to be met), while at the same time acknowledging the needs of the other person in the relationship.

Chapter 4: DBT for PTSD

"Healing doesn't mean the damage never existed. It means the damage no longer controls your life."—Akshay Dubey

---

In Chapters 1 and 2 (pages 14 and 31, respectively), you learned about PTSD and how it affects your brain chemistry and your life. In Chapter 3 (page 38), you discovered DBT, its concepts (Acceptance + Change), and core skills (Mindfulness, Distress Tolerance, Emotion Regulation, and Interpersonal Effectiveness). This chapter is where we bring everything together. Here, you'll learn how to use DBT skills for PTSD.

IMPORTANT: This chapter is full of DBT skills exercises that will help you with your mental healing recovery. But since PTSD is about trauma, please have your safety plans ready at all times. (An example of Safety protocols can be found on page 11.) Also, as you go through the exercises and think about your traumatic experience(s), remember that you survived them! That alone, dear reader, is a great thing.

Why DBT for PTSD?

Dialectical behavior therapy (DBT) was initially developed to help people with borderline personality disorder (BPD). So, why is DBT a good treatment method for PTSD? It's because many people with BPD also have PTSD, and vice versa.[49,50]

Now, even though people with BPD and PTSD show different symptoms, they also share similar indicators, such as:

- Inability to tolerate distress
- Difficulty regulating emotions
- Trouble forming and maintaining healthy relationships
- Engaging in self-destructive activities (e.g., self-harm, substance abuse, unhealthy eating habits, etc.)

Because of this, it is believed that DBT could also help people with PTSD; over the years, multiple studies have shown this was true.[51,52,53,54]

Avoidance and Radical Acceptance

Avoidance is a primary symptom of PTSD. There are two types of avoidance: *emotional avoidance* and *behavioral avoidance*.

- **Emotional avoidance** is when we try to stop ourselves from having thoughts or feelings about a traumatic event. This happens to us internally, and even people who know us well might not notice it at all. For example, a person who has been sexually assaulted may try to avoid unpleasant emotions like fear when they are reminded of the trauma.

- **Behavioral avoidance** is when we stay away from places, people, sounds, or smells that remind us of the traumatic event. For example, suppose you survived a major natural disaster (e.g., hurricane, tornado, earthquake, etc.). In that case, you might not want to go back to the place where it happened.

I think DBT's **Radical Acceptance** significantly addresses the PTSD symptom of avoidance. Studies show that *avoidance coping* is linked to anxiety and depression and makes people even more prone to stress[55,56,57,58], underlining Dr. Linehan's belief that *to avoid is to prolong suffering*.

I'm going to get a bit personal here. You see, I did A LOT of *avoidance coping* myself.

In high school, I would eat lunch in the library even though I wasn't allowed to. I did this because it hurt more to be seen eating alone in the cafeteria. In college, right in the middle of my loneliness and depression, I would every now and then get asked by my roommate about how things were going. I always replied, *"Great!"* When there was a party or event, I would act like I had "other plans." If I said yes to something, I would cancel at the last minute because my anxiety was so bad. (I'd get so worried about all the "bad" and "wrong" things that could happen if people saw me in a social setting.)

During therapy, I learned that *avoiding* doesn't mean I was fooling anybody. I can say, *"Great! I'm all good,"* till I was blue in the face, but that doesn't mean they believed me.

Yes, avoidance makes us feel better because it keeps us from facing our traumas, but a big part of that, at least for me, was about hiding. I tried to hide what I was going through. I didn't want anyone to find out. But here's the ugly truth I discovered—everyone close to me already knew.

I'm sharing this, so you'll know that if someone in your life asks you how you're doing or notices how you act and asks about it, it's not an attack. It's highly likely to be a sign of concern. This is why I found Radical Acceptance to be so freeing. Accepting my reality relieved me of the burden of hiding and denying.

So, are you ready to try Radically Acceptance? Let's clarify a few misunderstandings about this concept before you do.

Radical Acceptance IS NOT:

- **Agreement, approval, or consent.** The only thing you accept here is that something traumatic happened to you. You're not agreeing that it should have happened, not approving the event, and not saying you're "okay" with what happened.

- **Giving up or giving in.** When you radically accept reality, this does not mean that you don't want things to improve. It's the opposite. Acceptance is acknowledging where you are now because you know it's the first step to getting better.

- **Inaction.** Acceptance of reality doesn't mean you surrender to whatever life throws at you. You're not a hopeless observer of your own life; you're its creator. So you accept what happened and then work to make your life better.

- **About Others.** Radical acceptance is about your thoughts, emotions, and behavior concerning the traumatic event—no one else's. It may be that the trauma you experienced or witnessed was caused by someone. Still, it's not about understanding them, letting go of them, or even forgiving them. It's all about you.

Think of avoidance as a closed door. You stay away from that door because it reminds you of the trauma you experienced or witnessed. But healing is on the other side of that door. So, if you don't open that door and walk through it, you slow down or prevent your own healing and stay in your current misery (*prolonging your suffering*).

Now, **think of radical acceptance as a key**. It's what can give you the courage to open that door, walk through it, and start walking toward recovery.

"You can't move forward with anything in your life until there is radical acceptance." –Lady Gaga

Worksheet: Radical Acceptance of Trauma

Radical acceptance of trauma is like saying, *"Something terrible happened, and it hurts. But it already happened. I cannot go back and change any part of it. I have no control over the past. The only thing I can affect is the future."*

Take a minute and reflect on the above statement. When ready, write down your Radical Acceptance statement(s) regarding the traumatic event you experienced or witnessed.

Example:
Trauma: Losing your home and all your possessions in a hurricane.
Radical Acceptance Statement: Something so unexpected and painful happened that it's making me feel so hopeless and scared for the future. But it already happened, and it cannot be undone. Focusing on the past just prevents me from making the present better. So I accept what happened. It's no one's fault. I accept it.

Your turn:

____

____

____

____

____

____

____

____

____

____

____

____

____

Desire to Change

Many mental health problems stem from our inability to "move on" from where we are. We feel stuck and don't know what to do about it. In my opinion, willingness is NOT the issue. Often, the lack of skill (i.e., how to do it) stumps us.

Radical Acceptance of the trauma that happened is just one part of the equation. The rest is taking the necessary steps to CHANGE. It's only when we change that our life becomes better.

"You're not stuck. You're just committed to certain patterns of behavior because they helped you in the past. Now those behaviors have become more harmful than helpful.
The reason why you can't move forward is because you keep applying an old formula to a new level in your life.
Change the formula to get a different result."
– Emily Maroutian

The following DBT skills are the "change steps" or actions you need to take. We already discussed these skills in Chapter 3 (page 49). However, here, we'll discuss how you can apply them specifically for PTSD.

"Mindfulness is a pause. The space between stimulus and response: that's where choice lies.–Tara Brach"

Mindfulness is the PAUSE you need when PTSD symptoms occur. It may seem like things are happening too fast, and you have no control over your actions, but you do.

You see, what's happening is that you're reacting on instinct. You're not giving yourself time—a pause—to enable your brain to take stock of the situation before you act.

This is what Chito[‡‡], a reader, had to say: *"One Friday night, I was driving home from work when a yellow SUV cab ran a red light and hit my car full-on on the driver's side. They say it's a miracle I came out of the accident alive, and I know that's true, but I just couldn't bring myself back into a car after that. Each time I try, I feel the impact on my side all over again. I hear screeching metal that hurts my ears. My heart starts to pound uncontrollably, and I have a panic attack.*

I didn't drive for about three years. Since I was one of five brothers, all that machismo made the fact that I didn't drive a bit of a family joke, but I didn't care... until my wife got pregnant. I thought I really needed to get a grip on this because I won't be able to forgive myself if something happened, and I couldn't drive to get help or bring her to the hospital.

---

‡‡ *Name changed for privacy.*

One night, I just said to my wife that I thought I needed help. This is the first time I have talked about the car accident in three years and what I feel whenever I'm around a car. An uncle of hers was a psychotherapist, and it was he who introduced me to DBT.

I'll admit that I wasn't sure DBT was right for me. The minute he said "mindfulness," I think I did a mental eye roll. But I was already there, so I might as well listen to what he had to say, right? To make a long story short, I kept coming back, learned the skills, put them into practice, and got brave enough to drive the day my son was born. Today, I can fully drive again. I still have my moments, though. I don't think they'll ever be gone. Sometimes I think I can still hear metal screeching, and when I'm in a big group, I still worry that someone will trip, fall, or do whatever and ram me on the side, but I can handle these moments now."

When you are mindful, you are not in your past, nor are you in your future. You are simply in NOW. And **when you are in NOW,** the area of the brain that processes **emotions become less active,** and the area that aids in **rational thought and decision-making become more active**. This helps us learn how to control our emotions, including strong emotions like fear, anger, grief, and others.

In the following pages are numerous exercises to help you become more mindful. I recommend making at least one of them part of your daily routine.

Worksheet: 1:2 Breathing

Every time we breathe in, our cells get oxygen to make energy and eliminate toxins. Every time we breathe out, we get rid of the waste gas carbon dioxide. In addition to this exchange of gases, breathing is linked to our nervous system.

Depending on the speed and depth of our breathing, the inhales and exhales trigger either the "fight or flight" or "rest and digest" systems of the nervous system. We trigger the latter—rest and digest—with 1:2 breathing. By making our exhalations twice as long, we calm our nervous system.

1. Sit up straight on a chair, lie on a mat or on your bed, or just stand, whatever is most comfortable for you.

2. Inhale through your nose for a count of four (4), inviting your abdomen to inflate gently like a balloon as you breathe in.

3. Exhale through your nose for an eight (8) count, inviting your abdomen to deflate as you breathe out gently.

4. Do this for 3-5 rounds.

Worksheet: Nadi Shodhana (Alternate Nostril Breathing)

Anyone who has tried mindful breathing knows that "quieting the mind" is a very hard thing to do! This breathing exercise calms your nervous system and mind and helps you focus so that your mind doesn't wander off.

1. Sit up straight on a chair, lie on a mat or your bed, or just stand, whatever is most comfortable for you.

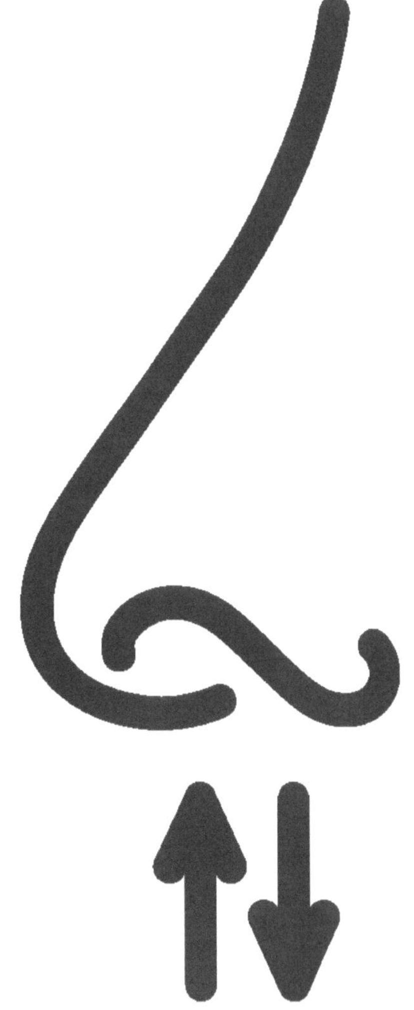

2. Put your right thumb over your right nostril to block the airflow.

3. Slowly *exhale* through your left nostril for a count of four (4).

4. When you're done exhaling, let go of your right nostril and put your ring finger on your left nostril.

5. Take a breath through the right nostril for a count of four (4). After you've taken a full breath in, let it out through your right nostril.

6. Let go of your ring finger and use your thumb to close your right nostril again.

7. Take a full breath in and let out a full breath from your left nose.

8. Repeat the whole process at least twice.

Worksheet: Wise Mind

Wise Mind (WM) is where *Emotional Mind* and *Reasoning Mind* intersect. WM is not something we create. We all have an emotional side and a logical side inside us. It's just that when faced with strong unpleasant emotions, we tend to react or behave based on these emotions[59]. During these moments, we fail to pause and consult our Reasoning Mind on what to do.

Note that acting based only on "logic" isn't a good idea because it means ignoring your or someone else's feelings. So what should you do? **Feel your emotions, but use reason before you do anything.** In other words, always act with Wise Mind.

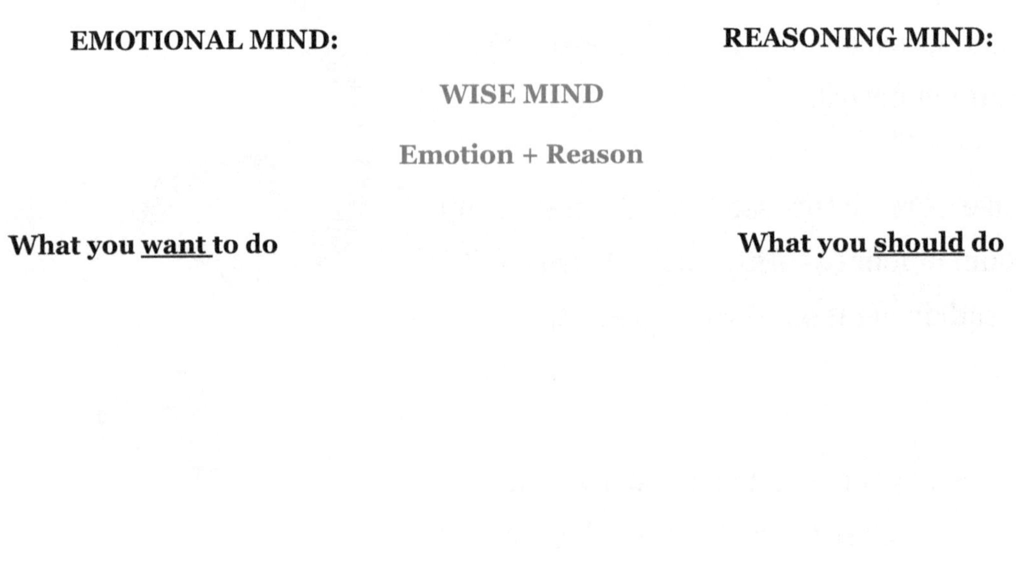

EMOTIONAL MIND:

REASONING MIND:

WISE MIND

Emotion + Reason

What you want to do

What you should do

The following reflective exercise will help you make consulting your Reasoning Mind a habit when faced with difficult emotions. This way, you can feel your emotions but don't necessarily have to behave according to them.

1. Think of a time when you did or said something you later regretted. Write down as much as you can about the event.

   Example: I pushed and shouted at my partner for asking me questions about my nightmares.

   Your turn:

   ___

   ___

   ___

2. Why did you do what you did?

   Example: I didn't want to talk about it. My partner's questions were making me angry.

   Your turn:

   ___

   ___

   ___

3. Why do you regret what you did?

   Example: Shouting was already bad, but to get physical? There's no excuse for that.

   Your turn:

   ___

   ___

   ___

4. How would you change things right now?

   Example: Instead of getting angry, I would tell my partner that I'm not ready to talk about my nightmares. I don't fully understand them myself and don't know how to deal with them.

   Your turn:

   ___

   ___

   ___

Notes: Your response to Question #1 refers to an instance of *Emotional Mind*. Your response to Question #3 is you consulting your *Reasoning Mind*. Your answer to Question #4 points to *Wise Mind*.

You are constantly refining your use of Wise Mind through introspection so consider additional circumstances in the past where you acted emotionally and what you would do differently today.

In the present, when you find yourself in a stressful situation, ask yourself, *"What would Wise Mind do?"*

Worksheet: Mindful Body Scanning

This exercise helps you calm down, organize your thoughts, and find your center.

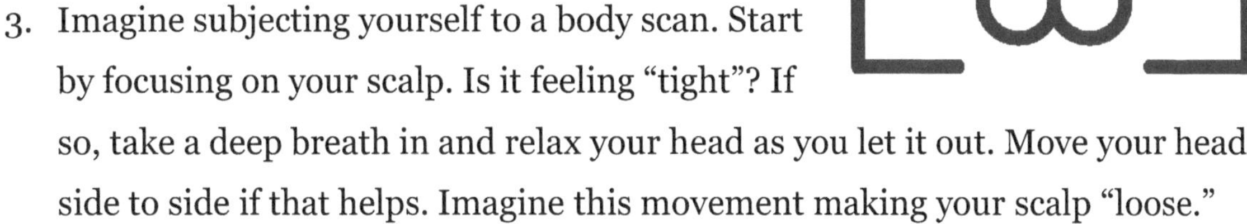

1. Lie on a mat, on your bed, or just stand whatever is most comfortable for you.

2. Box Breathe (page 53) for two cycles.

3. Imagine subjecting yourself to a body scan. Start by focusing on your scalp. Is it feeling "tight"? If so, take a deep breath in and relax your head as you let it out. Move your head side to side if that helps. Imagine this movement making your scalp "loose."

4. Move on to your forehead. Are you frowning? If so, take a deep breath and relax your forehead as you let it out. Release any tension.

5. Notice your eyebrows next. Are they meeting in the middle? If so, take a deep breath and relax your eyebrows as you exhale. Imagine them falling to the sides of your face.

6. Next, focus on your cheekbones. Are they warm? If so, breathe in and imagine a cool breeze touching your cheeks as you breathe out.

7. After checking all the aspects of your face, check your shoulders. Are they flat on the floor/mat/bed? If not, breathe in and out as you've done above.

8. Keep going until you've scanned and relaxed your whole body.

> *"You can't calm the storm, so stop trying. You can calm yourself. The storm will pass." – Timber Hawkeye*

If Mindfulness is taking a pause, then Distress Tolerance is like standing still and bearing the distress unpleasant emotions are causing. You do this NOT because you're okay with the situation but because you accept that you can't do anything about it.

The distress is already here. It cannot un-happen. But if you act according to your pain, it will worsen the situation, so the best you can do right now is to tolerate the distress.

My Distress Tolerance level was very low when I was dealing with OCD, GAD (General Anxiety Disorder), and depression. This meant that whenever I was upset, I showed my emotions right away by getting *angry*. This emotional impulse of mine did not help at all and made so many things in my life worse.

Thanks to DBT, I've increased my distress tolerance levels. I no longer act out and have learned the virtue of mentally and physically standing still for a moment.

The following DBT Distress Tolerance exercises will assist you in developing the necessary skills you need to tolerate high-stress situations. I hope they help you as much as they have helped me.

Worksheet: Into the Cold

Cold temperatures activate the *Mammalian Dive Response*, which triggers our parasympathetic nervous system, the network of nerves that tells the body to **slow down and relax**.[60]

Use this technique whenever you are experiencing a very distressing emotion (e.g., panic, fear, anger, anxiety, etc.) or have a strong urge to engage in dangerous behavior (e.g., violence, self-harm, use drugs, etc.).

CAUTION: Subjecting your face to cold water lowers your heart rate. If you have a heart condition or are allergic to freezing temperatures, please consult your physician before doing any of these exercises.

Because PTSD symptoms can happen at any time, you should have a plan for when you are at home or in public. I've started the table with a few ideas. If you like any of them, check them off. Of course, feel free to add your own ideas too.

AT HOME/ALONE	ELSEWHERE/WITH OTHERS
○ Go to the bathroom and splash cold water on your face.	○ Go to the bathroom and splash cold water on your face.
○ Go to the freezer, get a couple of ice cubes and hold them in your hand.	○ If it's winter, go outside and face the cold.
○ Fill a zip-lock bag with cold water and put it over your eyes and upper cheeks while holding your breath. (This tricks your brain into thinking you are underwater.)	○ If you have access to a refrigerator, bring a filled water bottle and put it in there. Grab it and pour the cold water over your face when in distress.
○ Take a VERY COLD shower.	○ If you have access to a refrigerator, keep a face gel mask cold pack in there and use it when necessary.
○ Fill a basin with cold water and submerge your face in it.	

Others:

Worksheet: STOP

When you're in distress, it's likely that you act rashly or impulsively without thinking. This is because you're in search of instant relief from the distress. But people often make things worse when they act without thinking, right? So, you have to stop yourself from (emotionally) reacting. The STOP exercise below will help you keep your cool (as opposed to being controlled by your emotions).

S	Stop
T	Take a step back.
O	Observe.
P	Proceed mindfully.

Following is an explanation of each acronym with some exercises where applicable.

S	Stop.

Stop! Imagine being "frozen" in time and place for a moment. Just exist. There's NO NEED to say or do anything at all. Stay in control by "freezing." This will prevent you from acting on your emotional impulses.

Example: It's New Year's Eve, but your trauma is related to gunshots. As a result, you can't bear to hear fireworks. However, your family doesn't understand this, and everyone is nagging you to join them outside. You're feeling stressed by all their coaxing. You're holding a drink in your hand, and you have this urge to throw it at someone's face, bang your fists on the table, and scream, "No!" But instead... you freeze in your tracks and do none of the above.

T	Take a step back.

Take a figurative and literal step back from the situation. Remove yourself from the circumstances until you feel calmer and more in control. Remember that no rule or code demands you reply at this exact moment. You are entitled to take a break from the situation.

Example: Imagine the New Year's Eve situation above. After freezing in your tracks, take a mental step back from whoever is trying to persuade you to check out the fireworks. Imagine "leaving the scene." Take a small (or big) physical step back, too, and say something like, "No, but thanks" or "Stop. I already said No to [family member]."

O	Observe.

Pay attention to what's going on inside and outside of you. Do this mindfully and without judgment. Observe facts. Observe only what's happening, not why or how things are happening.

Example of observing yourself: I am standing. I'm gripping the drink I have in my hand. My breathing is erratic.
Example of observing your surroundings: [Family member] said something and is looking at me, waiting for a reply. They're holding a drink and half-eaten pizza. My niece is trying to stay awake behind them.

What are you observing?

___

___

___

P	Proceed mindfully.

The previous steps have all been about getting the PAUSE your mind needs to calm down and assess the situation. Now, it's time to move forward and decide what you need to do.

To proceed mindfully, consult Wise Mind (page 98) and ask yourself, *"What do I want to happen?", "How can I prevent this situation from worsening for me and others?"*

Example: Your Aunt Lily is physically dragging you to join the fireworks activities outside. You're angry and feeling panicked at the same time. Your impulse is to roughly pull your arm from her and shove her away from you. But you don't want to make the situation worse, so you ***stop*** *(freeze) and take a mental and physical* ***step back*** *from your aunt. You* ***observe*** *that she's tipsy. Her face is red, and her speech is slightly slurred. You know that when Aunt Lily is drunk, there's no point arguing. She's likely not even going to remember this event tomorrow. So you* ***proceed mindfully*** *by slowly extricating your arm while helping her not to lose balance, telling her that you don't like fireworks, and leaving the room.*

Worksheet: ACCEPTS

Distraction is a great way to pull your attention *away* from distressful situations. The following distracting skills will help you divert your thoughts and emotions so that you don't act impulsively when in distress.

A	Activities.
C	Contributing.
C	Comparisons.
E	Emotions.
P	Push away.
T	Thoughts.
S	Sensations.

Following is an explanation of each acronym with some exercises where applicable.

A	Activities.

Make a list of activities you enjoy that demand your full attention. The objective is to completely lose yourself (be "in the zone") in any of these activities, diverting your attention from whatever or whoever is causing your distress. *Examples: go on a run, swim laps, solve a Sudoku puzzle, etc.*

List down as many focus-grabbing activities as you like below.

1. ______________________________
2. ______________________________
3. ______________________________

4. ____________________
5. ____________________
6. ____________________
7. ____________________
8. ____________________
9. ____________________
10. ____________________

C Contributing.

When we are in distress, we become very self-absorbed (e.g., *What's happening to me?, Why is this happening to me?, Why am I feeling this way?* etc.) A great way to distract yourself is to divert your attention from yourself to others. Studies show that considering others' needs and contributing not only helps the people you are helping but also helps you mentally and physically, making you healthier and extending your life span.[61] *Examples: go through your closet and find clothes to donate, arrange a food drive, donate your time (e.g., volunteer visiting the elderly at a local senior home), create a care package for a friend or family member in need, etc.*

What do you want to contribute? List as many ideas that come to mind.

1. ____________________
2. ____________________
3. ____________________
4. ____________________
5. ____________________
6. ____________________
7. ____________________
8. ____________________
9. ____________________
10. ____________________

C Comparisons.

Comparisons are also a way to take your mind off of yourself but in a slightly different way. Here, you're trying to see your situation more positively by comparing it to something worse that happened to you in the past. *Example: Two years ago, I had a panic attack that made me run to my car, leave my wife and toddler in the park, and drive dangerously into traffic. I side-swiped another vehicle and can't forget the fear I had inside at the thought that I might have killed someone. What I'm feeling now is nothing compared to that.*

Your turn:

____

____

____

E Emotions.

When you're in distress, what are you feeling? Anger? Fear? Frustration? Whatever it is, distract yourself by trying to provoke a completely different emotion from yourself. *Example: If you're afraid, read a feel-good book to feel happy. If you're angry, read a love letter or card you previously received to feel love.*

Your turn:

____

____

____

P	Push away.

When in distress, negative emotional urges arise. For example, if you're mad, you might want to throw something or hit someone. You might want to stand up and run away if you're panicking. PUSH AWAY these impulses by blocking any further thoughts about them. (**Important:** This activity should only be done to avoid making a situation worse. Please do not use it as your go-to technique when in distress because that can lead to *avoidance coping*, which is unhealthy.)

"Pushing away" is not about denying your emotions. It's about radically accepting your emotions (e.g., *I'm very uncomfortable with this group of people*) and then pushing away any emotional impulse you may have about it (e.g., *I will NOT shove the person next to me away.*)

Here are a few examples of "pushing away" activities you can adopt. Feel free to include your ideas as well.

- ☐ Find a quiet area where you can be alone, then shout "STOP!" (to any negative thoughts and emotional impulses you may have).
- ☐ Stay exactly where you are (freeze), and then build an imaginary wall between yourself and others in your mind.
- ☐ Snip it. Mentally place your urges in a box and then put that box in a far, far away place. Imagine the box going further and further each time you exhale.
- ☐ Others:

  ____

  ____

  ____

T | Thoughts.

Distract yourself with happy thoughts. *Examples: sing your favorite song in your head, imagine your favorite cartoon character, think about your favorite movie and what "role" you can play, etc.*

Your turn:

____

____

____

S | Sensations.

Distract yourself by submitting your body to various physical sensations. Here are a few examples. Feel free to include your ideas as well.

- ☐ Chew sour gum.
- ☐ Drink annoyingly sweet, sugary drinks.
- ☐ Open the freezer door and cool your face.
- ☐ Bite a chili pepper or throw a few pepper flakes in your mouth.
- ☐ Take a cold shower.
- ☐ Swim in an icy pool.
- ☐ Others:

  ____

  ____

  ____

Worksheet: PASS Kit (Panic Anxiety Stress Support Kit)

The PASS kit is a collection of calming and anti-stress objects developed by University of Waterloo students *Tina Chan* and *Alaaddin Sidahmed*. It's a mental health first aid kit that includes a stress ball, an eye mask, earplugs, flash cards (tips and exercises to decrease stress and anxiety), and a card listing various mental health crisis hotlines if you need help beyond what the kit can provide.

You can purchase the PASS kit online on their website. However, I would suggest creating your own to customize it to your needs. Your trauma is personal to you, and it's you who knows best what items can quickly ease your distress.

Here are a few sample items to put in your PASS kit to jumpstart ideas. As always, don't hesitate to add your own thoughts. **Important**: Don't make your PASS kit big. The kit should be something you can carry with you at all times.

- ☐ Cooling face gel mask.
- ☐ A miniature picture of ____________ (someone you love, admire, gives you strength, etc.)
- ☐ Chewing gum.
- ☐ Small stress ball.
- ☐ Small bottle of a scent that calms you.
- ☐ A rosary.
- ☐ Worry beads. (You can wear these at all times if this works for you.)
- ☐ Others:

  ____

  ____

  ____

  ____

  ____

Worksheet: TIPP

Distract yourself from distressing emotions by changing your body's chemistry. Each skill below causes your body's response patterns to change quickly, making you feel less emotionally agitated. Note that you don't need to do them all. For example, I usually do the *Intense Exercise* skill, and that's enough to calm me down.

T	Temperature.
I	Intense Exercise.
P	Paced Breathing.
P	Paired Muscle Relaxation.

Following is an explanation of each acronym with some exercises where applicable.

T	Temperature.

Calm down by subjecting yourself to cold temperatures. (See Into the Cold, page 103).

I	Intense Exercise.

Distract your mind (and ergo your emotions) by engaging in intense physical activities. Don't have much time? Use apps like the *5 Minute Home Workouts* by Olson Applications or *Seven – 7 Minute Workout* by Perigree AB to get in some quick workouts throughout the day.

P Paced Breathing.

When we're in distress, we tend to breathe fast and erratically. Calm yourself by pacing your breath. You can try Box Breathing (page 53), 1:2 Breathing (page 96), or Alternate Nostril Breathing (page 97).

P Paired Muscle Relaxation.

While doing Paced Breathing above, you can combine this with paired muscle relaxation. Here's what to do: When you take a deep breath in, slowly tighten your muscles, but not so much that they cramp. When you take a deep breath out, let all that tension go while telling yourself to relax.

Tip: Do this muscle flexing and relaxing as if you're doing a body scan. For example, flex and release your face muscles, then move on to your neck and shoulders. Next, flex and release your arms and hands, then move on to your core muscles. Continue until you reach your legs and feet.

"Feel the feeling but don't become the emotion. Witness it. Allow it. Release it." –Cristal Andrus

Remember this image?

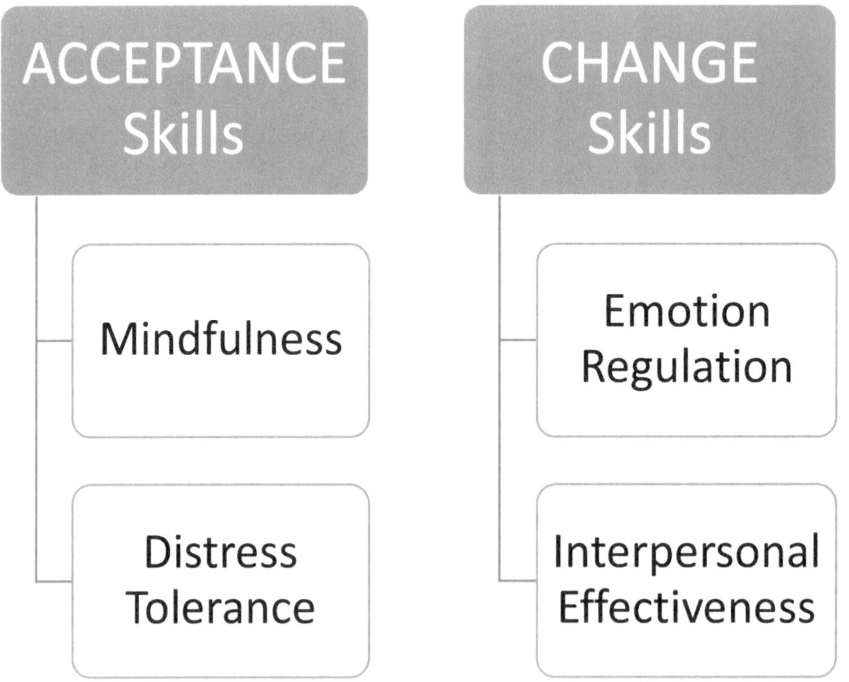

If Mindfulness is the pause we need (time to think), and Distress Tolerance is like standing still for a moment (to stop ourselves from acting out), then Emotion Regulation is where we start to change and learn new behaviors.

Note that Emotion Regulation is NOT emotion suppression. You're not denying or "putting a lid" on your distress or feelings here. You're going to Wise Mind (Emotional Mind + Reasoning Mind) so that you can control your emotions instead of your emotions controlling you.

Worksheet: Check the Facts

Check the Facts is an exercise where you stop, think, and check your feelings against the facts. This helps you understand what's happening instead of what you feel is happening.

First, let's do a reflective exercise. Think back on a few times when you acted too quickly (impulsively). It can also be something you thought was a big deal at the time but turned out not to be.

Question: What emotion do you want to verify? *Example: my fear*
Your answer:
Question: What happened? What caused this emotion? *Example: I went inside the living room and saw my son lying face down on the floor.*
Your answer:
Question: What presumptions did you have regarding the situation? What was your immediate thought? *Example: My son was dead.*
Your answer:

Question: What did you do?

Example: I screamed his name, ran to him, grabbed him up off the floor, and started to check him out.

Your answer:

Question: What happened afterward? What was the consequence of your actions?

Example: My son was crying because he got scared and hurt when I grabbed him. My wife ran from the kitchen to the living room, and she looked frightened and confused at what she saw.

Your answer:

CHECK THE FACTS:

You listed your assumptions above, but WHAT ELSE happened? What was the reality of the situation?

Example: My son was perfectly fine. He was just lying on his belly, playing with a toy I didn't see.

Your answer:

Question: Why do you believe you reacted the way you did? What were you scared of?

Example: My time in Afghanistan was rough, to say the least. I saw dead people, including children, on the ground every single day. When I saw my son like that, I immediately saw dead bodies in my head, and I felt an intense fear come over me.

Your answer:

Question: Looking back, on a scale of 0-5, did your emotion fit the facts? (0 = not at all, 5 = yes):

Example: 0, not at all

Your answer:

Question: What do you believe you could have done differently to avoid reacting impulsively (without thinking)?

Example: I should have taken a step back and looked around, really looked around, to realize where I was, which was in my own living room—not in Afghanistan.

Your answer:

Question: Since your emotion DID NOT fit the facts, what would you do differently? *Example: I would calmly call out to my son and say something like, "Hey bud, what are you doing on the floor?"*
Your answer:
Question: Would you do anything differently if your emotion fit or partially fit the facts? *Example: I'm not sure. If my son groaned in pain, I would run to him and lift him off the floor, but I probably would not have been so rough.*
Your answer:

IMPORTANT: **Check the Facts** is not limited to past events. You should apply this technique whenever you feel intense, unpleasant emotions. However, I recommend repeating the preceding practice at least two (2) more times. Consider previous incidents in which you may have overreacted and, as a result, made the situation worse. This is to acquaint you with the process of fact-checking your emotions.

Worksheet: Opposite to Emotion

Sometimes, we still have difficulty controlling our behaviour even when we fact-check our emotions and discover that they do not fit the facts. That is, we still want to do what we want, even though we know we may be overreacting!

To help stop yourself, an **Opposite to Emotion** table is provided below. **Column A** covers unhealthy feelings, **Column B** shows what you might ordinarily want to do when you experience these emotions, and **Column C** lists a counter-action to your natural inclination.

The next time you find yourself in a highly stressful situation, consult this table and do what you wrote in Column C. (I've done the first emotion as an example.)

A	B	C
Emotion	**Emotion-Driven Action**	**Opposite to Emotion**
What are you feeling?	*What you would ordinarily do in this situation.* *(If you have a natural desire to perform something other than what is described below, please write it down on a separate sheet.)*	*Make a list of actions that go entirely against how you feel.*
Fear	*Run away, avoid, get mad*	*Stay and talk; do some mindful breathing exercises; think happy thoughts*
Sadness	Binge-eat, drink alcohol	
Guilt	Shut down, self-criticize, or even blame others (deflect)	
Anger	Scream, sulk, or do something aggressive, such	

A	B	C
Emotion	**Emotion-Driven Action**	**Opposite to Emotion**
What are you feeling?	*What you would ordinarily do in this situation.* *(If you have a natural desire to perform something other than what is described below, please write it down on a separate sheet.)*	*Make a list of actions that go entirely against how you feel.*
	as slamming the door or breaking something	
Emptiness	Call and hook up with an ex	
Loneliness	Please people around me so they don't leave	
Frustration	Break something	
Helplessness	Cry, scream, punch someone or something, cut myself	
Resentment	Spread stories about someone	
Feel free to add more emotions and scenarios in the extra rows below.		

Worksheet: Problem Solving

You have fact-checked your emotions, and the situation fits the facts. You are justified in feeling what you're feeling. However, that does not mean you should still give in to your emotional impulses. For example, you start to talk to your partner about your PTSD. But instead of being understanding and supportive, they're invalidating or dismissing your experience. *"Oh, surely, it wasn't that bad?", "But that was years ago!"*

Their response hurts and angers you. You fact-checked your emotions, and yes, they are justified. Your instinct is to go over and slap your partner across the face. But... will that make things better? In all likelihood, it won't. So what do you do?

Now's the time to problem-solve the situation itself. The goal here is to **change the situation as a way to change your emotions**.

Question: What's the problem? Describe the situation that's causing your intense, painful, or unpleasant emotions. *Example: After finally getting the courage to open up about my PTSD, my partner is not taking me seriously.*
Your answer:
Question: Did you Check the Facts (page 117)? Y/ N If not, please do the Check the Facts exercise before proceeding.)
Question: What's the short-term goal here? What do you want to happen to feel that you've made progress in this situation? *Example: I want my partner to take this discussion seriously.*
Your answer:

TO-DO: List as many steps or solutions as possible to achieve your goal! Don't evaluate or judge your ideas. List anything that comes to mind that will help you improve this situation.

Example: (1) My partner's multi-tasking, so I have to ask them to sit and focus on what I say. (2) Repeat what I said, but be more direct. (e.g., This is very important to me. I need help.) (3) I probably picked the wrong time to talk to them about this because they just got home from work. I will take a break and talk about this again later when there are no distractions.

Your answers: (Use extra sheets if necessary.)

1. ________________________________

2. ________________________________

3. ________________________________

4. ________________________________

5. ________________________________

6. ________________________________

7. ________________________________

8. ________________________________

9. ________________________________

10. ________________________________

"Life is meant to be shared. We need each other."
– Lailah Gifty Akita

As mentioned, Mindfulness is the pause we need to be fully present in the moment. Distress Tolerance is the skill of bearing distress so that we don't act based purely on emotions. Emotion Regulation is taking steps to control our feelings instead of letting them control us. The last skill, Interpersonal Effectiveness, is finding, building, and keeping healthy relationships because we need these to lead fulfilling lives.

Now, relationships are not just about you. It's also about the other people in the relationship with you. However, we don't control other people, and we're not responsible for their behaviors. The only actions we're responsible for are our own. For this purpose, the Interpersonal Effectiveness skills you're about to learn in the following pages focus on YOU. Specifically, your needs and how you communicate them so that you find your needs met in the relationship.

Living with PTSD can be overwhelming, and it would help if you had the understanding, help, and support of others. Interpersonal Effectiveness enables you to achieve this while considering *their* wants and needs at the same time.

Recovering from Invalidation

In my own mental recovery journey, I've experienced three groups of people: those who (1) focus on you, (2) ignore you, or (3) invalidate you. I found the latter to be the most damaging.

There I was, finally having the courage to talk and seek help for my mental health problems, and some people would tell me things like, *"There's no such thing," "Get over it,"* or *"It can't be THAT bad."*

With PTSD, **traumatic invalidation** occurs when you're constantly being deliberately misunderstood, misread, or misinterpreted, when important facts regarding your trauma are being ignored or denied, or when your experiences (during and after the trauma) are being trivialized or denied.

So, what did I do?

Firstly, I radically accepted that invalidation hurts. Secondly, to deal with the pain I was feeling from being invalidated, I used Distress Tolerance techniques like 5-4-3-2-1 Grounding (page 60) and STOP (page 105). DBT also taught me that "invalidation is rarely a catastrophe" and that my truths and experiences are valid regardless of what others think or say.

And know too that you have influence in your relationships. Suppose someone invalidates you, but you still want to try to have a relationship with that person. In that case, you have nothing to lose by trying any of the skills below.

Worksheet: DEARMAN[§§]

You want your needs met in a relationship. However, there is an "art" to making your request(s) without damaging your relationships. **DEARMAN** is the skill to apply to achieve this goal.

D	Describe the situation.
E	Express how you feel.
A	Assert yourself.
R	Reinforce your request.
M	Mindfulness.
A	Appear confident.
N	Negotiate.

Following is an explanation of each acronym with some exercises where applicable.

D	Describe the situation.

What's going on? What do you want? Discuss the situation using clear and concise words. Don't say what you think or feel; stick to the facts.

Example: I am having a tough time right now, and the last thing I need is a 2-week vacation with my in-laws.

§§ *We already did this exercise on page 79. However, it's very good relationship exercise so I'm featuring it again here with PTSD-related examples.*

What's the situation?

E	Express how you feel.

Use "**I**" statements. Remember that what you're describing are *your* thoughts and emotions. **"You"** statements can be taken as accusations by the other person, increasing the chance for conflict. *Example: I get very stressed there with everyone around. It's not their fault. I just need time.*

Your turn:

A	Assert yourself.

Clearly express what you want to happen without being confrontational. The other person will understand you better as a result of this. *Example: So I don't want to accompany you and the kids when you go.*

Your turn:

R	Reinforce your request.

Make sure the other person knows how important your request is. So tell them how grateful you will be if they give you what you want or need. *Example: I know it's a big ask, but I would really appreciate the time alone to work on my issues. I would really appreciate your support.*

Your turn:

___

___

___

M	Mindfulness.

Keep your words and feelings in check, and no matter what the other person says, stay on topic. *Example: So, I hope you understand me. I need the time away on my own.*

Your turn:

___

___

___

A	Appear confident.

Convey confidence through your words and body language. Be sure of your request but don't be intimidating. For instance, do not stare other people down. Be consistent with your attitude too. For example, do not sit up straight while making your request and slouch afterward.

I had very low self-esteem, so appearing confident was something I had to practice a lot. For example, I walked looking down for years and had a bad "slouching posture." So I started practicing in front of the mirror, and I would stand and watch myself square my shoulders back. I also imagined a string on the top of my head that was pulling it upwards to prevent myself from looking down all the time. Next, I practiced what I wanted to say in front of the mirror. I slowly learned to use *fewer words* and be as direct (but polite!) as possible.

How do you want to show confidence?

____

____

____

____

N	Negotiate.

If the person you're speaking to is unwilling to accommodate your request, try negotiating. This will give you both a chance to devise a workable solution. You can suggest a course of action or inquire about what the other person believes should be done moving forward.

Example: How about I join you guys the last weekend, and then we can all go home together? What do you think?

Your turn:

____

____

____

Worksheet: GIVE

You need to **G.I.V.E.** to get. This exercise is all about effective communication. It teaches us how to say what we want in a way that makes others want to give us what we want.

G	Be Gentle.
I	Act Interested.
V	Validate.
E	Show an Easy Manner.

Following is an explanation of each acronym with some exercises where applicable.

G	Be Gentle.

When making your request, be gentle with your ways. Do not demand or be disrespectful. Also, avoid saying or doing anything that might offend the other person. In short, be nice!

List 5 ways you can ask for something in a ***gentle*** way. *Example: use a soft voice, start your sentence with "Would you do me a favor and..." or "Do you mind if..."*

1. ______________________________
2. ______________________________
3. ______________________________
4. ______________________________
5. ______________________________

I Act Interested.

If you want the other person to listen and consider your request(s), then you must show an interest in their response.

List 5 things you can do to show that you are ***interested*** and care about what the other person is saying. *Example: face the person speaking, maintain eye contact, respond to what was said, etc.*

1. ______________________________
2. ______________________________
3. ______________________________
4. ______________________________
5. ______________________________

Validate.

Recognize the other person's emotions and opinions with WORDS and ACTIONS. This way, you show that this is not a one-sided conversation.

List 5 things you can do to show ***validation*** to others. *Examples: say, "I understand this is difficult for you..." or "Let me see if I understand you correctly. You mean..."*

1. ______________________________
2. ______________________________
3. ______________________________
4. ______________________________
5. ______________________________

E Show an Easy Manner.

Display an easy manner so that the other person feels you're making a *request*, not a demand. When you have a friendly attitude, people will feel more at ease and be more open to what you want.

List 5 things you can do to display an ***easy manner*** to others. *Examples: use a little humor, smile, adopt a non-threatening demeanor (e.g., don't block the other person's way), etc.*

1. ____
2. ____
3. ____
4. ____
5. ____

Worksheet: FAST

This exercise is all about maintaining your self-respect during any interpersonal interaction. Remember, you're not the only one with needs in this relationship, and there will be times when the other person will also assert what they want. So how do you ask for what you want or say no to a request in a way that won't make you feel bad about yourself later? You apply the FAST technique.

F	Be Fair.
A	No Apologies.
S	Stick to your Values.
T	Be Truthful.

Following is an explanation of each acronym with some exercises where applicable.

F	Be Fair.

Be fair to yourself and the other person during the conversation. When you make your request, be sure it's not something above and beyond the other person's capability to grant such a request.

What's your request? Are you sure it's fair to ask this of the other party?

___

___

___

When someone asks you for something, ensure you're actively listening and genuinely considering their request.

How are you validating the other person in this conversation? (See **V** in GIVE for an example, page 131.)

A	No Apologies.

Don't apologize or over-apologize for anything. Don't say sorry for making a request, and don't say sorry if you say no to a request made of you.

Practice stating your request without apologizing:

Example: I would like to take Friday off.

Practice saying "No" to a request without apologizing:

Example: As much as I want to, I can't give you Friday off because of all our backlog.

S	Stick to your Values.

Don't give in just because the other person doesn't like or want to do what you want. Repeat your request assertively (but not rudely or threateningly). On the other hand, don't give in and say "Yes" to a request when you know it goes against your values.

Practice sticking to your values when making a request:
Example: I'd need Friday off anyway because I have a very important appointment with my therapist.

___

___

___

Practice sticking to your values and say "No" despite the other person's persuasion, nagging, convincing tactics, etc.
Example: I can't stay. I want to help, but this appointment is significant for my mental health.

___

___

___

T	Be Truthful.

Don't tell lies or overstate things to get what you want. Neither should you make false excuses just because you have difficulty turning down a request.

Practice being truthful when making a request:

Example: I've been very stressed at work and at home. Honestly, I don't feel like myself lately. That's why I need the day off.

____

____

____

Practice being truthful when saying "No:

Example: I won't be in Friday. I want to help with the backlog, but I've been very stressed at work and at home. Honestly, I don't feel like myself lately. That's why I need the day off.

____

____

____

Chapter Highlights:

- **Dialectical Behaviour Therapy** is a great way to help people with PTSD.
- **Radical Acceptance** addresses avoidance, which is a primary symptom of PTSD.
- **Change** in DBT begins when you understand and put into practice its four primary skills. For this purpose, **Mindfulness**, **Distress Tolerance**, **Emotion Regulation** and **Interpersonal Effectiveness** worksheets are provided.
- **Invalidation**: why it's hurtful, damaging to your mental health, and what you can do about it.

Chapter 5: Continuing the Road to Coping and Healing

"Your present circumstances don't determine where you go. They merely determine where you start."
– Dr. Lauren Fogel Mersy

We covered many things in this book. The first thing I hope you take away from it is that you DO NOT have to suffer indefinitely from the trauma you experienced or witnessed. I promise you, life can be good!

I've shared many DBT exercises to help you with your journey, and the following are a few more tips I'd like to share. They have helped me so much in my healing process, and I hope they do the same for you.

1. **Volunteer (contradict helplessness by helping!).** While going through my mental health problems, I would often be overcome by a feeling of helplessness, as if there's nothing I can do or say to improve things. I found volunteering to be very therapeutic. It gave me a purpose. It made me think of others instead of spending hours wallowing in my own misery.

   Volunteering doesn't have to be a BIG gesture. For example, you can volunteer to rake the leaves for an elderly neighbor or cook a pot of soup for a homeless shelter. For more ideas, you can visit sites like Idealist.org or VolunteerMatch.org

2. **Embrace Nature.** I never considered myself to be the "outdoorsy" type. Self-isolating indoors was my thing. Well, we already know that that didn't work, so I did the exact opposite—I went outside. Before long, I was hooked on nature. Being in nature helped me calm down, slow down, and be more mindful. It helped de-clutter my chaotic thoughts.

   If you live in the city, check local parks or visit community gardens nearby. You can also bring nature indoors. For example, add more plants inside your home, plant an herb garden on your balcony, etc.

3. **Get Moving.** Engaging in physical activities is underrated. The mind-body connection is real[62], and I've discovered that if I'm physically exhausted, my mind has no choice but to "de-activate." By the time I have the energy to think, I often realize that what I was so anxious about wasn't as bad as I initially thought they were.

   But don't over-exert and injure yourself. Start slow (but sure!) if you're currently leading a sedentary lifestyle or have not been active for a while. For example, if walking 10,000 steps a day is your goal, buy an inexpensive pedometer or use apps like Pacer or GoogleFit and work up to 3,000-5,000 steps per day. Once you've consistently reached that, add another 1,000 steps until you reach 10,000 steps.

   I aim to walk at least 6,000 steps daily, then I supplement that with resistance band training a few times a week and yoga on the days I don't weight train.

4. **Select and Protect Your Inner Circle.** In the space below, write down the people closest to you. Use more sheets if necessary. If you can only write down a few names, that's okay too.

My Current Inner Circle:

1) ______________________________
2) ______________________________
3) ______________________________
4) ______________________________
5) ______________________________
6) ______________________________
7) ______________________________
8) ______________________________
9) ______________________________
10) ______________________________

Now, take a long and hard look at the list you made. Do you trust these people completely? (*For example, can you confide in them about your PTSD?)* Do they really support you? Do they have your back? Are they loyal to you?

Chances are, not all are. And since social psychologists believe that we are the average of the five individuals we spend the most time with, choose your inner circle wisely.

Part of any mental healing journey is identifying your inner circle because it's best to have support. Yes, the changes must be your choice, and you're the one who needs to do the work, but support from others is essential. They help ease the load and can be your shield against pain, disappointments, vulnerabilities, and others.

Once you find these people, uphold them. Earn your right in their inner circle too.

5. **Learn to Say "Goodbye."** After doing tip #4 above, you might realize that there are people around you who are not positive influences at this time (or at all). In this case, be brave and end that relationship. Remember that you need all the positive energy you can get right now.

   Yes, this is easier said than done. It can be tough to cut people from your life, especially if they are family, but "goodbye" doesn't necessarily mean forever. You can re-evaluate the relationship later on if you feel there have been improvements.

   Here's what my friend Denise*** had to say: *"My oldest brother doesn't believe I have PTSD. He thinks I'm a drama queen and sneers during family events when I discuss therapy. I got tired of defending myself. So one day, I wrote him an email. I said I love him and always will, but I will be disengaging for now. I want to get better, and maybe later, we can reconnect."*

6. **Adopt a Pet.** Studies have shown that having a pet can help with mental health and well-being.[63,64] If your lifestyle situation permits it, consider adopting one. Dogs are known to be great pet choices because they read people well, are sympathetic, and make you go outside!

7. **Keep an Open Mind.** Despite today's awareness concerning mental health problems, many types of therapies people find dubious. My opinion is this: don't discount it until you've tried it. You never know what will work for you. Some alternative therapies are yoga, aromatherapy, music therapy, art therapy, journaling, acupuncture, etc. In addition to DBT, I do yoga each morning.

*** *Name changed for privacy.*

8. **Self-Monitor.** The DBT exercises in this book are roads to self-discovery. In addition, keep a journal where you can record anything and everything concerning your PTSD. For example, suppose you find yourself always nervous Friday nights. In that case, you can explore that further and take the necessary steps to ensure you don't feel that way (e.g., ensure you're not alone Friday nights, buy extra door locks, etc.).

9. **Find a Support Group.** Family and friends don't have to be your only source of support. Go online and offline and find PTSD support groups. Sometimes, the best people to help are those who know exactly what you're going through. Online, you can look for PTSD support groups on Facebook or reddit. Offline, you can consult with a doctor or psychotherapist and ask for PTSD support groups you can attend near you.

10. **Be kind and patient with yourself.** Everyone reacts to trauma in their own way, so it's important to go at your own pace. Years ago, I came across this advice: talk to yourself like you would to a dear friend, and I've been practicing it since.

11. **Seek Professional Help If You Need It.** Never shy away from professional help. If you feel like you're not progressing in your journey, then it's time to talk to a professional. If you find face-to-face therapy to be unavailable in your area or too costly for you, then consider online individual or group sessions like the ones provided by BetterHealth or ReGain as they can be more affordable.

Please go ahead and add your own ideas.

Chapter 6: Conclusion

Living with PTSD can be overwhelming. That's why I'm incredibly thankful to you for choosing this book to help you live a less stressful life and be less influenced by the trauma you've gone through.

Mental healing recovery is never a linear process. Life happens. We might hit a rough patch, and our mental health takes a step back—but that's okay. Remember, you are already a survivor! The next seconds, minutes, hours, and days are new, and it's up to you to determine how great they should be.

Here's a quick recap of what we covered in this book:

- Post-Traumatic Stress Disorder (PTSD): what it is, causes and symptoms, and currently known treatments.
- Living with PTSD: Understand how trauma affects the brain and how PTSD negatively affects your daily life.
- Dialectic Behavior Therapy (DBT) and its main fundamentals (Acceptance and Change) and its core skills (Mindfulness, Distress Tolerance, Emotion Regulation, and Interpersonal Effectiveness).
- DBT for PTSD: An in-depth presentation of DBT exercises you can use for PTSD.
- Additional self-care tips for living a less stressed life due to trauma.

Traumatic experiences change us; for some of us, those changes mean living unhappy lives—sometimes for years. But I want you to know that THERE IS HOPE.

Peace, *happiness*, *safety*, *security,* and other words you might not associate with your life now are within reach. You just need to decide now that you're willing to do the work to achieve them.

Appendix A – Trauma Resiliency[†††]

Check the boxes next to the ones that you think describe you best.

- ☐ I like to socialize, and I'm comfortable spending a lot of time with others.
- ☐ I like trying new things.
- ☐ I get along with everyone. (I'm not "difficult.")
- ☐ I have confidence in myself.
- ☐ I try to understand why things happen to me.
- ☐ I try to understand and break down bad situations into parts I can handle.
- ☐ I try to figure out how to deal with problems in my life.
- ☐ I'm an optimist, and I see more good than bad in everything and everyone.
- ☐ I like a good challenge, and when the time comes, I'm up to it.
- ☐ I can adjust to difficult situations easily.
- ☐ I have a good group of friends and people I can turn to for help.
- ☐ After a setback, I can quickly bounce back and pick up where I left off.
- ☐ I can laugh at myself.
- ☐ I appreciate myself.
- ☐ I feel like there is hope.
- ☐ I like to try new things and see things from different angles.
- ☐ I can handle a lot of things at the same time.
- ☐ I care about how other people feel.
- ☐ I'm not easily discouraged.
- ☐ I do my best to plan and structure my own life.

[†††] *Adapted from* van der Meer, C. A., te Brake, H., van der Aa, N., Dashtgard, P., Bakker, A., & Olff, M. (2018). Assessing psychological resilience: Development and psychometric properties of the English and Dutch version of the Resilience Evaluation Scale (RES). *Frontiers in Psychiatry*, 9. https://doi.org/10.3389/fpsyt.2018.00169

Question: What do you notice about yourself when you read these statements? Do you feel good? Do you get agitated? Do you reflect?

Answer:

___

___

___

Question: As you went through the list, did you notice any pattern about the items checked and not checked?

Answer:

___

___

___

The more you check, the more likely you are to do something about the trauma you experienced or witnessed and get through it.

Please note that the above scale just provides an indication of your resilience to trauma. It should not be taken as a replacement for a healthcare professional's official evaluation.

Appendix B – PTSD Self-Evaluation

Following is a list of difficulties adapted from the DSM-5 symptom criteria for PTSD[‡‡‡] that some people experience after a traumatic event.

Please read each one carefully. Are you experiencing or doing any of these? If yes, please rate how much it has bothered you <u>in the last month</u>.

1) Do you keep having disturbing, unwanted thoughts about the stressful event?

☐ Never	☐ Rarely	☐ Somewhat	☐ Often	☐ Very Often

2) Do you keep having disturbing, unwanted dreams about the stressful event?

☐ Never	☐ Rarely	☐ Somewhat	☐ Often	☐ Very Often

3) Do you have moments when you feel or behave as if the stressful event were repeatedly happening (*re-living* or *re-experiencing*)?

☐ Never	☐ Rarely	☐ Somewhat	☐ Often	☐ Very Often

4) Do you get very upset when something reminds you of your trauma?

☐ Never	☐ Rarely	☐ Somewhat	☐ Often	☐ Very Often

5) Are you experiencing severe bodily reactions (such as a racing heart, difficulty breathing, or sweating) when something brings up the stressful memory?

☐ Never	☐ Rarely	☐ Somewhat	☐ Often	☐ Very Often

---

‡‡‡ *Adapted from* Weather, F. W., Litz, B. T., Keane, T. M., Palmieri , P. A., Marx, B. P., & Schnurr, P. P. (2013). The PTSD Checklist for DSM-5 (PCL-5). Retrieved November 2, 2022. Scale available from the National Center for PTSD at www.ptsd.va.gov.

6) Are you trying to avoid memories, thoughts, or emotions related to the trauma you experienced?

☐ Never ☐ Rarely ☐ Somewhat ☐ Often ☐ Very Often

7) Do you try hard to avoid people, places, conversations, activities, or situations that remind you of the traumatic event?

☐ Never ☐ Rarely ☐ Somewhat ☐ Often ☐ Very Often

8) Do you have problems recollecting vital parts of the traumatic experience?

☐ Never ☐ Rarely ☐ Somewhat ☐ Often ☐ Very Often

9) Do you look negatively at yourself, others, or the world? For example, do you think things like, *"I am terrible," "I'm not loveable," "I trust no one,"* or *"There's no hope in this world"*?

☐ Never ☐ Rarely ☐ Somewhat ☐ Often ☐ Very Often

10) Do you blame yourself or others for the trauma you experienced?

☐ Never ☐ Rarely ☐ Somewhat ☐ Often ☐ Very Often

11) Do you often suffer from negative emotions such as anxiety, disgust, anger, remorse, or shame?

☐ Never ☐ Rarely ☐ Somewhat ☐ Often ☐ Very Often

12) Have you lost interest in activities you formerly found enjoyable?

☐ Never ☐ Rarely ☐ Somewhat ☐ Often ☐ Very Often

13) Do you feel distant or disconnected from others?

☐ Never ☐ Rarely ☐ Somewhat ☐ Often ☐ Very Often

14) Do you find it challenging to feel positive emotions such as *happiness* or *love* for others?

☐ Never ☐ Rarely ☐ Somewhat ☐ Often ☐ Very Often

15) Do you exhibit irritability, impulsivity, or violent behavior?

☐ Never ☐ Rarely ☐ Somewhat ☐ Often ☐ Very Often

16) Do you engage in excessive risk-taking or dangerous behavior?

☐ Never ☐ Rarely ☐ Somewhat ☐ Often ☐ Very Often

17) Do you feel "on edge" or "super alert"?

☐ Never ☐ Rarely ☐ Somewhat ☐ Often ☐ Very Often

18) Are you easily startled or feel "jumpy"?

☐ Never ☐ Rarely ☐ Somewhat ☐ Often ☐ Very Often

19) Do you have difficulty concentrating or focusing?

☐ Never ☐ Rarely ☐ Somewhat ☐ Often ☐ Very Often

20) Do you find it difficult to fall or remain asleep?

☐ Never ☐ Rarely ☐ Somewhat ☐ Often ☐ Very Often

Scoring:

0 = Not at all | **1** = A little bit | **2** = Moderately | **3** = Quite a bit | **4** = Extremely

Using the above scale, please tally up your score.

Your Score: ____________________________

Interpretation:

A score of 31–33 or higher suggests you might have PTSD and need treatment. A score between 31 and 33 *indicates* you don't meet the criteria for PTSD or are at the subthreshold of PTSD symptoms.

Important:

This 20-item **questionnaire does not replace a doctor or licensed mental health provider diagnosis.** However, the reality is that people don't get help because they're afraid their problems aren't real or "bad enough" to warrant professional help. After your self-assessment, if you believe you might have PTSD, please don't hesitate to talk about it with someone, a doctor, or a licensed mental health professional.

Appendix C – Establishing a Sleep Routine

Quality sleep can be elusive. Concerns, worries, and responsibilities often interfere with much-needed respite. Science shows, though, that a consistent sleep routine is critical for good physical, mental, and emotional well-being.[65] So here are some tips for you to do just that.

But before you establish a sleep routine, check your bedroom. Is it conducive to sleep? Is it a place that promotes relaxation and calmness? If not, make some changes. For example:

- Change bedroom curtains and bedsheets to a calming, non-stimulating color such as blue, green, or light yellow. (If necessary, repaint your room too.)
- Go for simple patterns or simple block colors. Bold designs and prints stimulate the mind, keeping you awake.
- Ensure that your pillows and mattress are comfortable. If not, now's the time to invest in new ones.
- De-clutter your bedroom. A messy bedroom can be distracting.
- Remove all electronic devices. These emit blue light, negatively affecting melatonin production (the "sleep hormone").[66]
- Keep the temperature cool. The best temperature for Rapid Eye Movement (REM) sleep, which is when you dream, learn, remember, deal with your emotions, and develop a healthy brain, is between 60 and 67°F. If your room is too hot or too cold, you'll keep waking up, preventing you from reaching this sleep stage.

Now that your bedroom is conducive to sleep, let's establish that sleep routine!

Top 3 Tips to Set a Sleep Routine

A sleep routine is a set of things you do every night in the same order, 30 to 60 minutes before bedtime. The following is what works best for me but feel free to create your own.

1. Based on your lifestyle, **set a specific bedtime** that you can adhere to most days of the week. *Example: 11:00 PM*

   The best time for me to go to bed is: ______________________________

2. What should you be doing **60 minutes before bedtime**? This might be the best time to start wrapping up your day. *Example: plan and prep breakfast for tomorrow, put things in the dishwasher, drink a calming tea, etc.*

   My 60-minute before-bedtime routine:

   # 1. ____

   # 2. ____

   # 3. ____

   # 4. ____

   # 5. ____

   # 6. ____

   # 7. ____

   # 8. ____

   # 9. ____

   # 10. ____

3. What should you be doing **30 minutes before bedtime**? For me, this is the stage when I really plan for sleep. *Example: brush teeth and do other bathroom rituals, put on sleeping pajamas, put a glass of water by the bedside, do 10-minute mindfulness meditation or stretching routine, spray pillows with lavender scent, turn off all the lights, and go to bed.*

My 30-minute before-bedtime routine:

1. ____________________

2. ____________________

3. ____________________

4. ____________________

5. ____________________

6. ____________________

7. ____________________

8. ____________________

9. ____________________

10. ____________________

Trauma-Related Worksheet: Better Sleep Using Your 5 Senses

In her book *Post-Traumatic Stress Disorder: A Clinician's Guide*, psychologist Matsakis states that "*sleeping problems are perhaps the most persistent of PTSD symptoms.*"[67]

Suppose you were traumatized while you were sleeping or in a bedroom. In that case, in addition to the above tips, you must figure out what about that bedroom or about sleeping is contributing to your sleeping problems today.

In this activity, you will use your five senses to help you find possible triggers in your bedroom or about sleeping. You don't have to be sure whether or not something is a trigger. Find the best way to sleep by observing and trying different things.

Use your sense of SIGHT. Is there anything you see in your bedroom triggering your trauma? *Example 1: If you sleep now in a room that's the same color as the room you experienced trauma in, you must change your current room's color. Change it even if that color is known to be "calming."*

Example 2: Look at the items in your bedroom. Is there anything at all that you think is triggering you? If so, remove it or make changes.

Here's what Frank[§§§], a reader, had to say: "I was 6 years old when a fire broke out in the middle of the night and engulfed our whole house. Mom and I lost my dad and baby brother that night. I've had sleeping problems since. During therapy as an adult, I discovered that one of my triggers was the alarm clock on my bedside table. When my dad woke me up and told me to run out of the house, I looked at the time on my alarm clock before I ran.

---

§§§ *Name changed for privacy.*

I have since then removed any clocks on my bedside table and anything else that would remind me of my childhood room."

Your turn:

____

____

____

____

____

Use your sense of HEARING. Are there sounds in your bedroom or around bedtime that may be triggering your trauma? *Example: If you're a war veteran and live in the city center, the loud sounds at night may trigger you. In this case, wearing earplugs or playing soothing music until you fall asleep might be ideal.*

Your turn:

____

____

____

____

____

Use your sense of SMELL. Are there scents in your bedroom that may be causing your sleep problems? *Example: Many people use lavender-scented soaps for bedsheets or spray a lavender mist in the bedroom since lavender enhances good, quality sleep.[68] However, if this was the scent in your bedroom when your trauma occurred, you should experiment with changing the scent or trying to sleep without any scent.*

Your turn:

Use your sense of TOUCH. Is there anything touching you while you sleep that may trigger trauma? *Example: If silk sheets play a role in your trauma, switch to another sheet fabric.*

Your turn:

Use your sense of TASTE. You may not be eating or drinking while you sleep, but what you consume or taste before bedtime can still affect you. *Example: What's the flavor of your toothpaste or mouthwash? A friend of mine related childhood sexual abuse to the minty scent and taste of her attacker. Part of her recovery was to eliminate all minty or citrusy aromas in her bedroom. She then switched her toothpaste and mouthwash to unflavored ones.*

Your turn:

Review Request

If you enjoyed this book or found it useful…

I'd like to ask you for a quick favor:

Please share your thoughts and leave a quick REVIEW. Your feedback matters and helps me make improvements to provide the best books possible.

Reviews are so helpful to both readers and authors, so any help would be greatly appreciated! You can leave a review here:

https://tinyurl.com/dbtptsd-review

Or by scanning the QR code below:

Also, please join my ARC team to get early access to my releases.

https://barretthuang.com/arc-team/

THANK YOU!

Further Reading

DBT Workbook for Adults

Develop Emotional Wellbeing with Practical Exercises for Managing Fear, Stress, Worry, Anxiety, Panic Attacks, Intrusive Thoughts & More

(Includes 12-Week Plan for Anxiety Relief)

Get it here:

https://tinyurl.com/dbtadult

Or by scanning the QR code below:

DBT Workbook For Kids

Fun & Practical Dialectal Behavior Therapy Skills Training For Children

Help Kids Recognize Their Emotions, Manage Anxiety & Phobias, and Learn To Thrive!

Get it here:

https://tinyurl.com/dbtkids

Or by scanning the QR code below:

DBT Workbook For Teens

A Complete Dialectical Behavior Therapy Toolkit

Essential Coping Skills and Practical Activities To Help Teenagers & Adolescents Manage Stress, Anxiety, ADHD, Phobias & More

Get it here:

https://tinyurl.com/dbt-teens

Or by scanning the QR code below:

DBT Anger Management Workbook

A Complete Dialectical Behavior Therapy Action Plan For Mastering Your Emotions & Finding Your Inner Zen

Practical DBT Skills For Men & Women

Get it here:

https://tinyurl.com/dbt-anger

Or by scanning the QR code below:

About the Author

Barrett Huang is an author and businessman. Barrett spent years discovering the best ways to manage his OCD, overcoming his anxiety, and learning to embrace life. Through his writing, he hopes to share his knowledge with readers, empowering people of all backgrounds with the tools and strategies they need to improve their mental wellbeing and be happy and healthy.

When not writing or running his business, Barrett loves to spend his time studying. He has majored in psychology and completed the DBT skills certificate course by Dr. Marsha Linehan. Barrett's idol is Bruce Lee, who said, "The key to immortality is first living a life worth remembering."

Learn more about Barrett's books here:
https://barretthuang.com/

Index

References

1 Wikimedia Foundation. (2022, October 31). *September 11 attacks*. Wikipedia. Retrieved November 1, 2022, from https://en.wikipedia.org/wiki/September_11_attacks

2 Peterson, S. (2018, October 22). *Secondary traumatic stress*. The National Child Traumatic Stress Network. Retrieved November 1, 2022, from https://www.nctsn.org/trauma-informed-care/secondary-traumatic-stress

3 Schlenger, W. E., Caddell, J. M., Ebert, L., Jordan, B. K., Rourke, K. M., Wilson, D., Thalji, L., Dennis, J. M., Fairbank, J. A., & Kulka, R. A. (2002). Psychological reactions to terrorist attacks. *JAMA*, *288*(5), 581. https://doi.org/10.1001/jama.288.5.581

4 Jiang, T., Webster, J. L., Robinson, A., Kassam-Adams, N., & Richmond, T. S. (2018). Emotional responses to unintentional and intentional traumatic injuries among urban black men: A qualitative study. *Injury*, *49*(5), 983–989. https://doi.org/10.1016/j.injury.2017.12.002

5 Roer, G. E., Solbakken, H. H., Abebe, D. S., Aaseth, J. O., Bolstad, I., & Lien, L. (2021). Inpatients experiences about the impact of traumatic stress on eating behaviors: An exploratory focus group study. *Journal of Eating Disorders*, *9*(1). https://doi.org/10.1186/s40337-021-00480-y

6 Maher, M. J., Rego, S. A., & Asnis, G. M. (2006). Sleep disturbances in patients with post-traumatic stress disorder. *CNS Drugs*, *20*(7), 567–590. https://doi.org/10.2165/00023210-200620070-00003

7 Babson, K. A., & Feldner, M. T. (2010). Temporal relations between sleep problems and both traumatic event exposure and PTSD: A critical review of the empirical literature. *Journal of Anxiety Disorders*, *24*(1), 1–15. https://doi.org/10.1016/j.janxdis.2009.08.002

8 Lien, C., Rosen, T., Bloemen, E. M., Abrams, R. C., Pavlou, M., & Lachs, M. S. (2016). Narratives of self-neglect: Patterns of traumatic personal experiences and maladaptive behaviors in cognitively intact older adults. *Journal of the American Geriatrics Society*, *64*(11). https://doi.org/10.1111/jgs.14524

9 Dijkstra, M. T., & Homan, A. C. (2016). Engaging in rather than disengaging from stress: Effective coping and perceived control. *Frontiers in Psychology, 7*. https://doi.org/10.3389/fpsyg.2016.01415

10 American Psychological Association. (n.d.). *Cognitive behavioral therapy (CBT) for treatment of PTSD*. American Psychological Association. Retrieved November 1, 2022, from https://www.apa.org/ptsd-guideline/treatments/cognitive-behavioral-therapy

11Shapiro, F., & Laliotis, D. (2010). EMDR and the Adaptive Information Processing Model: Integrative Treatment and Case Conceptualization. *Clinical Social Work Journal, 39*(2), 191–200. https://doi.org/10.1007/s10615-010-0300-7

12 *Va.gov: Veterans Affairs*. How Common is PTSD in Adults? (2018, September 13). Retrieved November 3, 2022, from https://www.ptsd.va.gov/understand/common/common_adults.asp

13 *Worldwide prevalence of PTSD*. NeuRA Library. (2021, October 27). Retrieved November 3, 2022, from https://library.neura.edu.au/ptsd-library/epidemiology-ptsd-library/prevalence-epidemiology-ptsd-library/worldwide-prevalence/

14 Grasso, D., Boonsiri, J., Lipschitz, D., Guyer, A., Houshyar, S., Douglas-Palumberi, H., Massey, J., & Kaufman, J. (2009). Posttraumatic stress disorder: the missed diagnosis. *Child welfare, 88*(4), 157–176.

15 Riddle, J. (2018, November 25). *PTSD symptoms in women: Unnoticed and undiagnosed - psycom*. PSYCOM. Retrieved November 3, 2022, from https://www.psycom.net/PTSD-symptoms-women

16 Gagnon-Sanschagrin, P., Schein, J., Urganus, A., Serra, E., Liang, Y., Musingarimi, P., Cloutier, M., Guérin, A., & Davis, L. L. (2022). Identifying individuals with undiagnosed post-traumatic stress disorder in a large United States civilian population – A machine learning approach. *BMC Psychiatry, 22*(1). https://doi.org/10.1186/s12888-022-04267-6

17 Sherin, J. E., & Nemeroff, C. B. (2011). Post-traumatic stress disorder: The neurobiological impact of psychological trauma. *Dialogues in Clinical Neuroscience, 13*(3), 263–278. https://doi.org/10.31887/dcns.2011.13.2/jsherin

18 Lynch, P. J., & Jaffe, C. C. (2020). *Ptsd brain*. Wikimedia. Retrieved November 3, 2022, from https://commons.wikimedia.org/wiki/File:PTSD_brain.svg. Original version licensed under Creative Commons Attribution 2.5 License 2006

19 Zotev, V., Phillips, R., Misaki, M., Wong, C. K., Wurfel, B. E., Krueger, F., Feldner, M., & Bodurka, J. (2018). Real-time fmri neurofeedback training of the amygdala activity with simultaneous EEG in veterans with combat-related PTSD. *NeuroImage: Clinical*, *19*, 106–121. https://doi.org/10.1016/j.nicl.2018.04.010

20 Akiki, T. J., Averill, C. L., Wrocklage, K. M., Schweinsburg, B., Scott, J. C., Martini, B., Averill, L. A., Southwick, S. M., Krystal, J. H., & Abdallah, C. G. (2017). The Association of PTSD symptom severity with localized hippocampus and amygdala abnormalities. *Chronic Stress*, *1*, 247054701772406. https://doi.org/10.1177/2470547017724069

21 Arnsten, A. F. T., Raskind, M. A., Taylor, F. B., & Connor, D. F. (2015). The effects of stress exposure on prefrontal cortex: Translating basic research into successful treatments for post-traumatic stress disorder. *Neurobiology of Stress*, *1*, 89–99. https://doi.org/10.1016/j.ynstr.2014.10.002

22 MediLexicon International. (n.d.). *Gaslighting: What it is, long-term effects, and what to do*. Medical News Today. Retrieved November 3, 2022, from https://www.medicalnewstoday.com/articles/long-term-effects-of-gaslighting

23 Bontempo, A. C. (2022). The effect of personalized invalidation of symptoms by healthcare providers on patient depression: The mediating role of self-esteem. *Patient Education and Counseling*, *105*(6), 1598–1605. https://doi.org/10.1016/j.pec.2021.09.034

24 Mushtaq, R. (2014). Relationship between loneliness, psychiatric disorders and physical health ? A review on the psychological aspects of loneliness. *JOURNAL OF CLINICAL AND DIAGNOSTIC RESEARCH*. https://doi.org/10.7860/jcdr/2014/10077.4828

25 Lee, S. L., Pearce, E., Ajnakina, O., Johnson, S., Lewis, G., Mann, F., Pitman, A., Solmi, F., Sommerlad, A., Steptoe, A., Tymoszuk, U., & Lewis, G. (2021). The association between loneliness and depressive symptoms among adults

aged 50 years and older: A 12-year population-based Cohort Study. *The Lancet Psychiatry*, *8*(1), 48–57. https://doi.org/10.1016/s2215-0366(20)30383-7

26 Steen, O. D., Ori, A. P., Wardenaar, K. J., & van Loo, H. M. (2022). Loneliness Associates strongly with anxiety and depression during the COVID pandemic, especially in men and younger adults. *Scientific Reports*, *12*(1). https://doi.org/10.1038/s41598-022-13049-9

27 Sareen, J. (2014). Posttraumatic stress disorder in adults: Impact, comorbidity, risk factors, and treatment. *The Canadian Journal of Psychiatry*, *59*(9), 460–467. https://doi.org/10.1177/070674371405900902

28 Fox, V., Dalman, C., Dal, H., Hollander, A.-C., Kirkbride, J. B., & Pitman, A. (2021). Suicide risk in people with post-traumatic stress disorder: A cohort study of 3.1 million people in Sweden. *Journal of Affective Disorders*, *279*, 609–616. https://doi.org/10.1016/j.jad.2020.10.009

29 Hori, H., & Kim, Y. (2019). Inflammation and post-traumatic stress disorder. *Psychiatry and Clinical Neurosciences*, *73*(4), 143–153. https://doi.org/10.1111/pcn.12820

30 Linehan, M. (2015). *DBT skills training manual*. The Guilford Press.

31 Carey, B. (2011, June 23). *Expert on mental illness reveals her own fight*. The New York Times. Retrieved August 1, 2022, from https://www.nytimes.com/2011/06/23/health/23lives.html

32 Linehan, M. M. (2015). *DBT Skills Training Manual*. The Guilford Press.

33 Maddux, W. W., Adam, H., & Galinsky, A. D. (2010). When in Rome ... learn why the Romans do what they do: How multicultural learning experiences facilitate creativity. *Personality and Social Psychology Bulletin*, *36*(6), 731–741. https://doi.org/10.1177/0146167210367786

34 Ratner, P. (2022, April 19). *Want happiness? Buy experiences, not things, says a Cornell psychologist*. Big Think. Retrieved November 3, 2022, from https://bigthink.com/neuropsych/want-happiness-buy-experiences-not-more-stuff/

35 Franke, H. (2014). Toxic stress: Effects, prevention and treatment. *Children, 1*(3), 390–402. https://doi.org/10.3390/children1030390

36 Wiebe, J. (2021, May 3). *The good stress: How eustress helps you grow.* Talkspace. Retrieved November 3, 2022, from https://www.talkspace.com/blog/eustress-definition-good-stress/

37 American Psychological Association. (n.d.). *APA Dictionary of Psychology.* American Psychological Association. Retrieved November 2, 2022, from https://dictionary.apa.org/emotion

38 Levine, G. N., Cohen, B. E., Commodore-Mensah, Y., Fleury, J., Huffman, J. C., Khalid, U., Labarthe, D. R., Lavretsky, H., Michos, E. D., Spatz, E. S., & Kubzansky, L. D. (2021). Psychological health, well-being, and the mind-heart-body connection: A scientific statement from the American Heart Association. *Circulation, 143*(10). https://doi.org/10.1161/cir.0000000000000947

39 Sawhney, V. (2021, August 6). *Weirdly true: We are what we eat.* Harvard Business Review. Retrieved November 3, 2022, from https://hbr.org/2021/08/weirdly-true-we-are-what-we-eat

40 Fox, N. (2022, February 1). *The many health risks of Processed Foods.* LHSFNA. Retrieved November 3, 2022, from https://www.lhsfna.org/the-many-health-risks-of-processed-foods

41 Hecht, E. M., Rabil, A., Martinez Steele, E., Abrams, G. A., Ware, D., Landy, D. C., & Hennekens, C. H. (2022). Cross-sectional examination of ultra-processed food consumption and adverse mental health symptoms. *Public Health Nutrition, 25*(11), 3225–3234. https://doi.org/10.1017/s1368980022001586

42 Zinczenko, D. (2019). *Eat This Not That!: The best (& the worst) foods in America.* Ballantine Books.

43 Maltz, M. (1960). *Psycho-Cybernetics* (First). Simon & Schuster.

44 Watson, N. F., Badr, M. S., Belenky, G., Bliwise, D. L., Buxton, O. M., Buysse, D., Dinges, D. F., Gangwisch, J., Grandner, M. A., Kushida, C., Malhotra, R.

K., Martin, J. L., Patel, S. R., Quan, S., & Tasali, E. (2015). Recommended amount of sleep for a healthy adult: A joint consensus statement of the American Academy of Sleep Medicine and Sleep Research Society. *SLEEP*. https://doi.org/10.5665/sleep.4716

45 Almondes, K. M., Marín Agudelo, H. A., & Jiménez-Correa, U. (2021). Impact of sleep deprivation on emotional regulation and the immune system of healthcare workers as a risk factor for covid 19: Practical recommendations from a task force of the Latin American Association of Sleep Psychology. *Frontiers in Psychology*, *12*. https://doi.org/10.3389/fpsyg.2021.564227

46 World Health Organization. (n.d.). *Physical activity*. World Health Organization. Retrieved November 18, 2022, from https://www.who.int/news-room/fact-sheets/detail/physical-activity

47 Umberson, D., & Karas Montez, J. (2010). Social Relationships and Health: A flashpoint for health policy. *Journal of Health and Social Behavior*, *51*(1_suppl). https://doi.org/10.1177/0022146510383501

48 Tough, H., Siegrist, J., & Fekete, C. (2017). Social Relationships, mental health and wellbeing in physical disability: A systematic review. *BMC Public Health*, *17*(1). https://doi.org/10.1186/s12889-017-4308-6

49 Pagura, J., Stein, M. B., Bolton, J. M., Cox, B. J., Grant, B., & Sareen, J. (2010). Comorbidity of borderline personality disorder and posttraumatic stress disorder in the U.S. population. *Journal of Psychiatric Research*, *44*(16), 1190–1198. https://doi.org/10.1016/j.jpsychires.2010.04.016

50 Frías, Á., & Palma, C. (2014). Comorbidity between post-traumatic stress disorder and borderline personality disorder: A Review. *Psychopathology*, *48*(1), 1–10. https://doi.org/10.1159/000363145

51 Steil, R., Dyer, A., Priebe, K., Kleindienst, N., & Bohus, M. (2011). Dialectical behavior therapy for posttraumatic stress disorder related to childhood sexual abuse: A pilot study of an intensive residential treatment program. *Journal of Traumatic Stress*, *24*(1), 102–106. https://doi.org/10.1002/jts.20617

52 Bohus, M., Dyer, A. S., Priebe, K., Krüger, A., Kleindienst, N., Schmahl, C., Niedtfeld, I., & Steil, R. (2013). Dialectical behaviour therapy for post-

traumatic stress disorder after childhood sexual abuse in patients with and without borderline personality disorder: A randomised controlled trial. *Psychotherapy and Psychosomatics*, *82*(4), 221–233. https://doi.org/10.1159/000348451

53 Harned, M. S., Korslund, K. E., & Linehan, M. M. (2014). A pilot randomized controlled trial of dialectical behavior therapy with and without the dialectical behavior therapy prolonged exposure protocol for suicidal and self-injuring women with borderline personality disorder and PTSD. *Behaviour Research and Therapy*, *55*, 7–17. https://doi.org/10.1016/j.brat.2014.01.008

54 Bohus, M., Kleindienst, N., Hahn, C., Müller-Engelmann, M., Ludäscher, P., Steil, R., Fydrich, T., Kuehner, C., Resick, P. A., Stiglmayr, C., Schmahl, C., & Priebe, K. (2020). Dialectical behavior therapy for posttraumatic stress disorder (DBT-PTSD) compared with Cognitive Processing Therapy (CPT) in complex presentations of PTSD in women survivors of childhood abuse. *JAMA Psychiatry*, *77*(12), 1235. https://doi.org/10.1001/jamapsychiatry.2020.2148

55 Cronkite, R. C., Moos, R. H., Beckman, E. E., & Leber, W. R. (1995). Handbook of depression.

56 Grant, D. M. M., Wingate, L. R. R., Rasmussen, K. A., Davidson, C. L., Slish, M. L., Rhoades-Kerswill, S., Mills, A. C., & Judah, M. R. (2013). An examination of the reciprocal relationship between avoidance coping and symptoms of anxiety and depression. *Journal of Social and Clinical Psychology*, *32*(8), 878–896. https://doi.org/10.1521/jscp.2013.32.8.878

57 Elliot, A. J., Thrash, T. M., & Murayama, K. (2011). A longitudinal analysis of self-regulation and well-being: Avoidance personal goals, avoidance coping, stress generation, and subjective well-being. *Journal of Personality*, *79*(3), 643–674. https://doi.org/10.1111/j.1467-6494.2011.00694.x

58 Penley, J. A., Tomaka, J., & Wiebe, J. S. (2002). *Journal of Behavioral Medicine*, *25*(6), 551–603. https://doi.org/10.1023/a:1020641400589

59 Jung, N., Wranke, C., Hamburger, K., & Knauff, M. (2014). How emotions affect logical reasoning: Evidence from experiments with mood-

manipulated participants, Spider Phobics, and people with exam anxiety. *Frontiers in Psychology*, *5*. https://doi.org/10.3389/fpsyg.2014.00570

60 Kyriakoulis, P., Kyrios, M., Nardi, A. E., Freire, R. C., & Schier, M. (2021). The implications of the diving response in reducing panic symptoms. *Frontiers in Psychiatry*, *12*. https://doi.org/10.3389/fpsyt.2021.784884

61 Dossey, L. (2018). The Helper's High. *EXPLORE*, *14*(6), 393–399. https://doi.org/10.1016/j.explore.2018.10.003

62 Pally, R., & Olds, D. (2018). Emotional processing: The mind-body connection. *The Mind-Brain Relationship*, 73–104. https://doi.org/10.4324/9780429482465-4

63 Brooks, H. L., Rushton, K., Lovell, K., Bee, P., Walker, L., Grant, L., & Rogers, A. (2018). The power of support from companion animals for people living with mental health problems: A systematic review and narrative synthesis of the evidence. *BMC Psychiatry*, *18*(1). https://doi.org/10.1186/s12888-018-1613-2

64 Grajfoner, D., Ke, G. N., & Wong, R. M. (2021). The effect of pets on human mental health and wellbeing during COVID-19 lockdown in Malaysia. *Animals*, *11*(9), 2689. https://doi.org/10.3390/ani11092689

65 Lunsford-Avery, J. R., Engelhard, M. M., Navar, A. M., & Kollins, S. H. (2018). Validation of the sleep regularity index in older adults and associations with cardiometabolic risk. *Scientific Reports*, *8*(1). https://doi.org/10.1038/s41598-018-32402-5

66 *Blue Light has a dark side*. Harvard Health. (2020, July 7). Retrieved November 3, 2022, from https://www.health.harvard.edu/staying-healthy/blue-light-has-a-dark-side

67 Matsakis, A. (1994). *Post-traumatic stress disorder: A complete treatment guide*. (L. Tilley, Ed.). New Harbinger.

68 Lillehei, A. S., Halcón, L. L., Savik, K., & Reis, R. (2015). Effect of inhaled lavender and sleep hygiene on self-reported sleep issues: A randomized controlled trial. *The Journal of Alternative and Complementary Medicine*, *21*(7), 430–438. https://doi.org/10.1089/acm.2014.0327